'audacious writing with something here for everyone . . . moments on every page that keep narrative tension bubbling away.' **Rohan Wilson, *Weekend Australian***

'An entertaining and thought-provoking romp with authentic dialogue with characters that are all complex and multidimensional . . . Rose writes with emotional intuition [and] has that eminently readable interiority that only a novel can bring.' **Louise Swinn, *Saturday Paper***

'*Bruny* throbs with the clash of rapacious development versus a simpler life . . . Crisp and evocative writing makes this a hugely enjoyable page-turner.' ***Marie Claire***

'Heather Rose takes no prisoners in this hugely entertaining satirical novel.' ***Readings***

'Among her intense political intrigues and deep concerns about the directions Australian society is taking Rose inserts moments of deep tranquillity . . . often passionately didactic and cautionarily disquieting, Bruny is thoroughly entertaining and endearingly Tasmanian.' **Katharine England, *The Advertiser***

'An expert storyteller, Rose has mastered the contemporary realist novel . . . Is there nothing she cannot do with her words and skilled imagination? No vignette or internal dialogue is here that doesn't enhance the complex tale she is making . . . Believable, relatable people, families, romance, grief and the terser political narrative all come together with magnificent brio.' ***The Age* and *Sydney Morning Herald***

'*The Museum of Modern Love* is more than just that rare treat, a book that requires something of the reader – it is a book that painstakingly prepares you for its own requirements. In a playful way, this bold new novel by Heather Rose is an astute meditation on art, bravery, friendship, love, how to live, and on dying . . . Once the novel is closed there is so much left to consider, leaving the reader at the start of a journey but well-equipped.' **Louise Swinn,** *The Age*

'If Heather Rose's audacious and beautiful new novel were adapted for the stage, it would require a theatre-in-the-round treatment . . . That Rose's novel evokes such a vivid mental staging is a testament to her powers as a storyteller. One of the delightful surprises of *The Museum of Modern Love* is discovering that the all-knowing storyteller is not your distant, narrative god descended from Dickens and Austen, but an intimate voice, someone we all recognise from our own struggles and lives. Pondering the parameters of this storyteller turns out to be almost as tantalising in this book as mulling its deeper questions: What are we? What is art? How should we live?' **Dominic Smith, author of** *The Last Painting of Sara de Vos*

'Framing a love story around a long-durational performance work, where the passage of time is essential, is a profoundly original idea. I loved this book.' **Marina Abramović**

'This captivating work explores the meaning of art in our lives and the ways in which it deepens our understanding of ourselves . . . Rose also combines intriguing characters with a laser-sharp focus on art to produce a gem of a novel.' *Library Journal,* **starred review**

'Clever, genre-bending . . . A portrait of human desire and human failing, but perhaps most profoundly, human striving for something greater than self. Rose's melancholy book resonates with emotion, touching on life's great dilemmas – death, vocation, love, art.' *Publishers Weekly,* **starred review**

'Deeply involving . . . profound . . . emotionally rich and thought-provoking.' *Booklist,* **starred review**

'From its conception to its last page, this book challenges our perceptions of where life ends and art begins . . .' *The Australian*

'The narrator's voice gives the novel a quiet power, as if the universe was filled with a non-meddling benevolence. There's a cinematic quality too, with even minor figures sketched in with sure and affecting touches. *The Museum of Modern Love* is alive with the surprise and challenge of presence in many of its forms – it is a very generous book indeed. Images and storytelling have been intertwined since the first human beings gathered by a painted wall to tell tales in the firelight. Heather Rose's *The Museum of Modern Love* works with these ancient ghosts with exquisite care and intelligence. Positing grief and art as deep echoes that corroborate the transitory nature of our lives, Rose brings the reader to a place of acceptance despite the inevitable darkness. With rare subtlety and humanity, this novel relocates the difficult path to wonder in us all.' *The Christina Stead Prize 2017*

'A meditation on love and creativity . . . Special kudos to the author for a pedantry-free examination of art's ability to change lives – and for this novel's tacit implications of the vanishing space between fact and fiction.' *New York Journal of Books*

'A moving book that invites the reader to revel and re-evaluate.' *Booktopia*

'Rose brings a skilled and at times almost mischievous artistry, not least in effecting narrative surprises that both disorient and persuade.' *Sydney Review of Books*

'A glorious novel, meditative and special in a way that defies easy articulation.' **Hannah Kent, author of** *Burial Rites*

'*The Museum of Modern Love* is that rare and lovely thing: a novel of ideas that blooms into a persuasive illusion of real life . . . The lapidary brilliance of Rose's sentences is never overblown and her style is one of prescient, unflustered beauty.' *West Weekend Magazine*

Heather Rose is the Australian author of eight novels. Heather's most recent novel, *Bruny*, won the ABIA 2020 General Fiction Book of the Year. Her seventh novel, *The Museum of Modern Love*, won the 2017 Stella Prize. It also won the 2017 Christina Stead Prize and the 2017 Margaret Scott Prize. It has been published internationally and translated into numerous languages. Both *The Museum of Modern Love* and *The Butterfly Man* were longlisted for the International Dublin Literary Award. *The Butterfly Man* won the Davitt Award in 2006, and in 2007 *The River Wife* won the international Varuna Eleanor Dark Fellowship. *Bruny* and *The Museum of Modern Love* are both in development for the screen, and the play of *The Museum of Modern Love* premiered at Sydney Festival in 2022. Heather writes with Danielle Wood under the pen-name Angelica Banks and their *Tuesday McGillycuddy* children's series has twice been shortlisted for the Aurealis Awards for best children's fantasy. Angelica Banks is also published internationally. Heather lives by the sea in Tasmania.

www.heatherrose.com.au

HEATHER ROSE

nothing bad ever happens here

ALLEN&UNWIN
SYDNEY • MELBOURNE • AUCKLAND • LONDON

First published in 2022

Copyright © Heather Rose 2022

  This project has been assisted by the Australian
Government through the Australia Council,
its arts funding and advisory board.

Allen & Unwin
Cammeraygal Country
83 Alexander Street
Crows Nest NSW 2065
Australia
Phone: (61 2) 8425 0100
Email: info@allenandunwin.com
Web: www.allenandunwin.com

*Allen & Unwin acknowledges the Traditional Owners of the Country on which we
live and work. We pay our respects to all Aboriginal and Torres Strait Islander
Elders, past and present.*

*The author also acknowledges the traditional owners and custodians of the land and
waterways of lutruwita where she lives and works, extending her deepest respects to
Tasmanian Aboriginal people, past and present, and acknowledges their sovereignties in
land, sea and sky, never ceded.*

 A catalogue record for this
book is available from the
National Library of Australia

ISBN 978 1 76106 632 0

Typeset in 13/18 pt Granjon LT by Bookhouse, Sydney
Printed and bound in Australia by Griffin Press

10 9 8 7 6 5 4 3 2 1

 The paper in this book is FSC® certified.
FSC® promotes environmentally responsible,
socially beneficial and economically viable
management of the world's forests.

For Mum

In some cases, names and narrative have been changed to protect the identities of those who may not have wanted to be written about or chose to remain anonymous.

SKY

May I speak to you
Like we are close
And locked away together?

HAFIZ

Here she is, standing in the schoolyard. She is six years old, dressed in a crisp green uniform. Other children are on the swings and seesaw, but she has taken herself off to stand alone under the eucalyptus at the edge of the playground. She gazes up through its broad branches to the sky above.

Hello, she says. *I'm ready. Tell me what to do. Make use of me.*

She might have chosen to do this at the small church where she attends Sunday school, but instead she does it here, because it feels as if this big tree must have a direct connection to whoever is in charge.

Does anyone answer back? They do not. Yet she feels better for having declared herself willing to be of service. She has reported for duty.

—

1

Physicists now know that 70 per cent of the known universe is dark energy. Dark matter is another 25 per cent. Once we thought we knew all about life, but it turns out everything we think of as reality is less than 5 per cent.

Crumpets and honey, hockey sticks, sailing boats, temples, shopping centres, literature, the pharmaceutical industry, mathematics, every scientific discovery, every plant, animal or virus below the sea and above, the planets and the stars we can name and all those we can't, this galaxy and the 200 billion other galaxies that comprise the known universe, everything that has been created, constructed, calculated, measured or observed by humans amounts to a mere fragment of existence. Ninety-five per cent is hidden from us, invisible, unknown, only to be imagined or sensed. Yet it's present everywhere, in every moment, in everything around us, and everything that *is* us.

—

Believing and belonging occupy a great deal of human life. What to believe? How to belong? All of it is a mystery that we fill with stories.

Standing under that tree in my primary school playground is not my first memory, yet it remains vivid. I will grow up and travel the world, and I will travel the inner places of heart and mind, always curious. What is this thing called life? Why am I here?

For decades now, I've asked strangers if something ever happened that they couldn't explain. Something outside the normal. To my surprise, I discovered that everyone had a story of a guiding hand, a strange connection, a reassuring presence, something life-saving or life-affirming, something more than a coincidence. Everyone had experienced something that gave them a sense that there was more to life than could be seen, touched or verified.

I could write a memoir about travelling, the writing life, or my love of baking cakes. But I'm still that girl under the tree who wants to get to the big conversation, to the heart of things. So here are some stories about life and death. About experiences that have no easy explanation, but which happened, nevertheless. The unknown, that 95 per cent – maybe it's an invitation for compassion. Life is a process of forgiveness for the choices we make in order to be ourselves.

FIRE

Here is where memories begin.

My mother is on a ladder watering the roof of our orange-brick house with a hose. The house is newly built and overlooks a wide blue river. I live on an island at the end of the world, just a week's sailing from Antarctica, though I do not know this because I am only two and a half years old. I do know, however, that my mother standing on a ladder and watering the roof is not a normal thing.

I hear her gasp. The forested hill behind us has become a wall of flames, a ridge of leaping red and amber spiralling up into billowing clouds. It is 7 February 1967. The wind blowing across Tasmania, birthed in the lizard heat of Central Australia, has become a firestorm travelling at more than 130 kilometres an hour, dropping millions of sparks. There is no rural fire service in 1967, nor a volunteer service. There is a small fire station over the hill but it has only limited equipment.

I am delivered to the home of our neighbours down the street while my mother retrieves my two older brothers from school. A goat, a sheep and chickens are in the neighbours' laundry. In their lounge room, I sit beneath a clothes horse and breathe in the scent of drying linen as I eat a delicious oatmeal biscuit.

By 3 pm the sky is black and the city of Hobart has emptied. The temperature is 40 degrees. Across our sylvan state there are flames hundreds of feet high, fireballs, exploding gum trees, roaring wind, melting roads. The power is out and communications are down. My dad is home early from work. He and a friend go to fight a fire nearby, using sacks to beat back the flames. Mum and my brothers return and soon everyone in our small community gathers on the beach to stand in the sea. Huge particles of ash fall about us.

In one day, fires burn through some 652,000 hectares of land; 1300 homes are incinerated, and 7000 people become homeless; 64 people die and more than 900 are injured. It takes three months for the power to be reconnected across suburbs and rural areas.

———

Our house does not burn down, nor do those of our friends and neighbours on the perimeter of the forest. Six months after the fire, I turn three, and six weeks after that, my mother gives birth to my sister. Now we are four children: two boys and two girls. My mother reads aloud to me as she breastfeeds my baby sister, turning page after page of Little Golden Books and *Mother Goose* until, one day, the words from her voice match the words on the page, and I am reading too.

—

At age four I am at the kitchen table scrawling squiggly line after squiggly line across a page with a crayon. My mother asks me why I am ruining the butcher's paper she's given me to draw on.

'I'm writing,' I reply brusquely.

It is lucky that I begin writing early because I have a long way to go. I've done many jobs in my life, but writing has always been my favourite thing to do. It's also been the hardest. It's required the greatest discipline, the longest hours and the deepest commitment. Writing has said: *Look more closely, go this way, dig deeper, learn this, know yourself better.* It has been a pathway into the unknown, the fascinating, the heartbreaking and the wonderful. I give myself to writing and it bends me, sharpens me, whittles me and sculpts me.

—

But first I am very young. My mother's voice is high and musical. She recites limericks, smokes cigars at parties and has an extensive repertoire of rude jokes. She loves The Goons, Monty Python and Walter Mitty. She makes her clothes from French *Vogue* patterns. She makes our clothes, too – even our school uniforms. Her sense of the ridiculous, her delight in the silly, is infectious. I am often in paroxysms of laughter. She can draw anything and make it look real. As a teenager she wanted to become a graphic artist, but there was no money for further study. When my younger sister begins kindergarten, my mother returns to work as a secretary. Along with a career, four children and a husband, she bakes and cooks, sews, preserves, sings, embroiders, gardens, arranges flowers, decorates cakes, and makes kayaks and pottery. Only on Sunday night does she forsake her culinary wizardry and feed us cheese on toast or Heinz tomato soup. (Anything from a packet or a tin is a treat in our house.) She is slender, elegant, dark-haired and beautiful. She gets chest infections and her back is often sore.

My father is handsome, reserved and serious. Dad grew up poor and started full-time work at fourteen. In his twenties, he completed high school by attending night school. Later, much later, I will ask him why he stayed in the tax department for forty years when he wanted to do other things. He tells me that he was making a bridge for his children from the lower class to the middle class.

Dad loves reading and music. My mother loves music, too. She is an atheist while Dad is a Christian. He takes us to church while Mum stays home. He is an introvert while she is an extrovert. She leans politically right, he leans left. Mum is sunny while Dad can be moody. He whistles when he is displeased and retreats into silence.

From Monday to Friday, Dad catches the 7.45 am bus to work in the city. Until they build the new highway, the journey takes almost an hour. A bus returns him home again by 6.10 pm. I watch out for it and run down to meet him, walking home holding his hand.

—

Childhood is kelp and sand, birds and sky, and boats pulled up from the tide. Rainy days are for reading in bed, playing games, cooking, doing craft. If it is fine, we are sent outside to play. There are seasons, weekly library trips, the radio playing in the kitchen, the fire at night and the habit of growing things. Everyone in our cul-de-sac grows things. We have a vegetable garden that provides much of our food, and a Golden Delicious apple tree in our backyard. Roses of every scent and colour line our front boundary, as if our surname requires it.

Our house is the first on a new subdivision above a curve of beachside shacks. We are surrounded by farms, apricot orchards, paddocks and dams. Throughout the sixties and seventies, a new house is always being built, a new family moving in. Kerbs and bitumen arrive, washing lines and paling fences. Our neighbours are public servants, business people, stay-at-home mums, teachers, academics, architects and retirees. There is a small government primary school.

Both sets of grandparents live close by, as well as cousins from Dad's side of the family. We children roam the farmland that is yet to become suburbia, building forts in sandy embankments, climbing the seaside cliffs, catching tadpoles in the dams, kicking the footy on the oval, playing beach cricket, swimming in the sea, exploring rock pools and riding our bikes everywhere like mad things. In winter we take cardboard and slide down the icy paddock behind the house. Only rarely does it snow, down there so close to the sea, and when it does we are awestruck.

There are neighbourhood barbecues, bonfires and fireworks, fancy-dress parties and dinners where the adults walk between homes for various courses, my mother's laughter rippling on the night air. On hot days, Mum and her girlfriends lie on the beach, laughing and chatting, rolling their eyes at the habits of their husbands, while we children swim, play and listen. There are Boxing Day gatherings down the street where a television broadcasts the start of the Sydney to Hobart yacht race. Days later these yachts sail up our river to the finish line. We watch them from our house, taking turns at the telescope. We do not own a television. Books and games, music and friends, the radio and the outdoors are our entertainment.

My brothers and I, and children who live along the way, walk to school together, a kilometre and a half each way. No one locks their doors. We are welcome in everyone's houses. We must be home by the time the streetlights come on.

—

The River Derwent is an enormous river travelling more than 200 kilometres from its birthplace in the highlands until it passes through Hobart beneath the watchful gaze of Mount Wellington. It can appear benign, but the river is quixotic, changing from calm to asperous in moments.

From our house, I watch the sun rise on the river's far shore washing the sky in tangerine, vermilion, peach and gold. Throughout the day, clouds stride in from the west, full and white, lean, brindled, feathered. On breathless mornings, the river is liquid satin. In winter it is wreathed in a high rolling fog. Full-moon tides crash below my bedroom window, low tides leave sand flats that mirror the sky. Seagulls and shorebirds wander the water's edge. Mount Wellington, always in view, changes from grey to blue to mauve throughout the day, until sunset turns the mountain into a silhouette. Every day there is a breeze, or many breezes. Tasmania is a place of endlessly changing weather.

As a child, I love the sea. I often spend dawn and dusk with my grandfather, waiting for the tug on my handline that signifies flathead, perch and, sometimes, a stripy trumpeter. I am mesmerised by light catching on ripples, by birds sliding across the sky and wind bringing its own shadow.

Solitude becomes my friend early: reading in bed late into the night; drifting on the swing in the backyard staring at clouds; sitting on the rocks by my grandparents' boatshed or on the shore below the family shack. At night I pull back the curtains to watch the moon rise over the river and wonder at all those stars. Every night I listen to the waves, the ceaseless metronome of my early years.

One day, when I am five, my mother mentions that her family came to Tasmania from Scotland a long time ago. I ask her where Scotland is. She says it's on the other side of the world. There is a globe in the lounge room which I love to spin, my fingers tracing the countries and oceans. For the first time, I grasp that I am at the bottom of this globe. Scotland is a long way away, far over the curve. I decide that as soon as I am grown up, I will go there.

All this lies at the heart of who I will become.

MOON

The best is perhaps what we understand least.

C.S. LEWIS

My dad's parents, Nan and Pa Rose, live across the road from the primary school in a small white two-bedroom weatherboard cottage with large green plaster frogs and several colourful gnomes in the front yard. During the week, I go there for lunch with my brothers and, when they move on to high school, with my little sister. After school finishes for the day, we return to Nan's until Mum finishes work and picks us up.

I hardly remember eating a school lunch brought from home. Instead, I am always at Nan's table eating Irish stew, corned beef, roast lamb, shepherd's pie. There is always jelly and custard, and sometimes there is a block of ice cream in a white cardboard wrapper. There is also apple pie, apple crumble, apple charlotte, apple snow or baked apples. I love food. Nan says that one day, when I am walking back to school, she'll hear a great pop and it will be my stomach exploding. Luckily, I have hollow legs.

———

This is my last memory of Pa. We are repeating a ritual he and I go through many lunchtimes. I am sitting on his lap at the kitchen table while Nan is serving up. Pa is trying to get me to plant a kiss on his cheek but the stubble is sharp against my lips, so I refuse.

He says, 'How many kisses are you going to give me today? Ten?'

I giggle and say, 'No!'

'Nine?'

'No!'

'Eight?'

'No!'

Until he gets to: 'Zero kisses?'

And I say, 'YES!'

Then I hug him tight around his neck and we both laugh.

After lunch, my sister and I walk back to school. While we are gone, an ambulance arrives. School finishes for the day and, unaware of what has happened, we return to Nan's. Someone – I don't remember who – tells me Pa is dead. It is 29 October 1975 and I am eleven years old.

Pa could balance his false teeth on the end of his tongue and make them chatter. He had the gravelly voice of a smoker, and wore a blue singlet over his expanding belly. He called the toilet on the back deck his 'throne' and spent long periods of time there reading *Reader's Digest* magazines. During the week he was a linesman for the PMG – the precursor to Telstra. On Saturdays, ever since his children were small, Pa went to the local RSL, where he drank from opening until closing.

I had sat on Pa's lap to see men walk on the moon. Pa echoed Neil Armstrong's words to me as we watched that staticky black-and-white film of men in spacesuits planting a flag: 'That's one small step for man, one giant leap for mankind.' Now it was Pa who had taken a really giant leap. He had died.

Nan and Pa's house was on the main road, so we weren't allowed to play in the short driveway. But that day, after I hear those words – 'Pa is dead' – I go out the front door and stand in the drive. I need to be alone and I know no one will look for me there. It occurs to me that you can die between lunch and after school. Death can come really quickly. This feels like an important thought.

After a while, I go back inside, through the kitchen and out onto the back porch. There is a lily patch at the bottom of the stairs, but everything else in the garden is edible or feeds things that are edible. The vegetable beds run north–south and east–west. The chooks and a compost bed are to the far right. The sun is catching on the cabbage leaves and silvering the potato foliage. The chooks are clucking. Corn is growing against the back fence near the gooseberries and raspberries. Tomatoes have just been planted. Bees are humming, butterflies are fluttering, carrots are busy underground. I realise things go on just the same after you are dead.

Inside the house, it is unsettled with visitors. Nan Rose is the warmest, softest, kindest person I know, but I can't find her. Maybe she is in the embrace of others, maybe she is at the hospital. Somehow the death of Pa makes Nan disappear, so I talk to the parrot.

Cocky is a big, green-feathered bird prone to outbursts of conversation and the occasional snap at our fingers when we feed him sunflower seeds. He lives in a cage on the back porch outside the laundry. I tell him Pa is dead. Perhaps he remembers a girl with short black hair saying to him, 'It's okay. Nan will still look after you. But you have to be nice to her. She might be sad.'

Nan isn't sad after Pa dies. In the coming weeks and months, she seems to breathe a sigh of relief. She starts saving for cruises, putting coins in a large cookie jar shaped like a priest that bears the words *Thou shalt not get fat*. I hear her say to a girlfriend, 'Saints preserve us, I lived through that. I hope I get to live long enough to enjoy myself.'

Nan lives for another eleven years. She takes several cruises. Then she, too, dies of a heart attack. Cocky outlives Pa and Nan. He goes to live with a neighbour across the road. I visit him there once. He might be alive still.

After Pa's death, Dad sits in the lounge room with the curtains closed playing mournful classical music.

I creep in. 'Are you okay, Dad?'

'Heather, dear, there's nothing you can do. I'm just very sad.'

'About Pa?'

'Yes.'

We are both quiet.

Dad borrowed Hemingway's *The Old Man and the Sea* from the library for me when I was six years old. It fired my imagination and broke my heart. I'd never read a book without a happy ending and I'd grieved for Santiago and the marlin. Now, sitting beside my dad on the patterned vinyl sofa, I discover what grief feels like at close hand, in someone I love. Grief is when nothing can be done and there's no going back to fix it, and there's no going forward without knowing that it can never be fixed. In another year I will learn that grief is more than a feeling. It's a wound that breaks open again and again.

SALT WATER

There must be something strangely sacred in salt.
It is in our tears and in the sea.

KHALIL GIBRAN

Grandad Burgess, Mum's dad, builds a tiny shack for us on the Tasman Peninsula, 120 kilometres from home. Nubeena is a small farming hamlet of rolling green hills looking down onto a narrow inlet of cliffs and bays. There is a long white beach five minutes through the bush. Our shack is not on the main beach but on the tidal bay behind it. All around is bracken, gum trees and sea. At low tide there are mudflats and at high tide a luminous tranquillity.

The shack is low-roofed with various uneven levels. There is step down into the bedroom where Nan and Grandad sleep, and a step up into the bathroom where the water is heated by a copper. The floors are covered in linoleum and seagrass matting. On the mantelpiece above the open fireplace, an alarm clock rests permanently at ten minutes to eleven. Grandad says that way it is always time for a little something. Fruitcake, short-bread, gingerbread . . .

We camp in the front yard in a big canvas tent. Then my parents build a fibro sleepout near the tank stand with a bedroom and two small bunk rooms. We go to the shack the day after Christmas, and we are there for Easter, on long weekends and through the school holidays.

The shack has only two water tanks, which often run low, so we swim all year round. Once a week, Mum heats water in the copper for a bath. A few inches of water must suffice for four children. There is an outside toilet that is home to vast civilisations of huntsman spiders, and an outside fire where we barbecue.

We run wild at the shack, tearing through the bush, always watching out for snakes. Tasmania is home to two of the most venomous snakes in the world – the tiger snake and the copperhead black snake. Neither worry us particularly; they are simply something to avoid on tracks, where they curl in pools of sunlight, or on the unpaved roads where they stretch out looking like shadows cast by the forest.

On wet days we play cards and board games, read books and tramp about outside in raincoats. On fine days we swim for hours, ride our bikes, climb trees and squelch in plastic sandals on the muddy shoreline. We sit on the narrow wooden jetty Grandad built and kick our legs above the incoming tide. We visit the wilder beaches and slide down sand dunes. Often our footprints are the only ones for miles.

We fish at dawn and dusk. We eat rabbits and wallabies hunted by Grandad, Dad and my brothers. Shellfish grow on the rocks below the shack. At low tide, I take a chisel from the shed and go down to the shore. I lever open oysters, dropping their plump dark-fringed bodies into my mouth. When Mum finds me there, she calls me her little seagull.

At the shack, we live with two sorts of ghosts. The embankments on the shoreline are middens packed with seashells, relics of the Indigenous people almost effaced by colonial Tasmania. When he points these out to me, Grandad says, 'See? Other people lived here. Other people loved it here long before we did.' He shows me pathways and clearings in the bush and says, 'See how they walked here. See how they slept there.' In the state museum in Hobart, there is a diorama showing a glowing campfire and an Aboriginal family gathered around it. The people are plaster, the fire a red electric light and the background a large painted scene of a bay. This scene fascinates me because it looks just like our bay at Nubeena.

Convict remains are evident, too. We are not far from Port Arthur, one of the most notorious prisons of the British penal system. We find house foundations long overgrown with bracken, each orange brick marked with the thumbprint of a prisoner.

—

Often when Grandad and I are out in the dinghy, each with a fishing line in our hands, he looks up at the sky, at the sun cresting the hills or slipping away in the west, at seabirds circling, the shimmering dawn refracting off the water, and says, 'Look, Heather, that's what beauty is.'

When we walk in the bush, he says, 'Always turn around and see which way you've come – that way you'll know the way back.' He makes me stop and cover my eyes with my hands. He turns me around a few times, and when I'm allowed to look again, he asks me which way is north, west, south, east. He has me look at the sun and guess what time it is. He teaches me about moon phases, tides, the direction of the wind, clouds that herald rain or a sunset that warns of a storm. He teaches me to see in the dark, to create simple traps in the bush and, of course, he teaches me to fish. He tells me that one night he was out fishing alone and a UFO shot out of the water only a hundred yards away and flew up into the sky. He says it was huge, made no sound other than the splitting of the water, and was gone in seconds.

'It scared the living daylights out of me,' he says.

Grandad Burgess is not a man given to the fantastic or make-believe. He is a barber by trade and, before I was born, ran an illegal bookie operation from the back of his salon on the wharf in Hobart. Apparently, it was successful enough to buy all the furniture for their home. Later, Grandad moved his salon to a shopping centre, but he never gave up on the horses. When I take a drive with him and Nan, Grandad stops their little blue Volkswagen beetle somewhere overlooking a stretch of coast then he turns on the car radio to listen to the races. He and Nan stare out to sea, Grandad urging on whatever name is carrying his bet. Sometimes he hands me the form guide and lets me choose a horse.

—

Nan Burgess, Mum's mum, is silver-haired with sapphire blue eyes, high cheekbones and pale peachy skin. Across her throat, she has a long white scar, the remnant of a goitre operation. Thyroid deficiency was common in Tasmania when she was young. The operation damaged her larynx, giving her voice the raspiness of a Dickens character. Nan can cut a person down with that voice. With just a word or two, she can reduce us to silence and better behaviour.

Nan is lean, wiry, snappy and full of opinions, mostly about the ways in which the world could be improved or small children could be improved. The term 'she does not suffer fools' was invented for Nan Burgess. She has a repertoire of harumphs and sniffs, a Morse code that punctuates our lives. Both our nans give love through food. Nan Rose's food comes with a warm hug. Nan Burgess's, delicious though it is, comes with a sense that we may be scolded in the near future for an act of stupidity. Grandad often assures us that her bark is worse than her bite.

—

Grandad is devoted to Nan, and she, frosty to all the world, is his co-pilot. She is clever with numbers. She wanted to go to university to study mathematics, but it wasn't done back then, so she started work in a shop. During World War II, she kept the accounts for a department store – the equivalent of Myer these days – but had to relinquish the role when the manager came home from the war. 'That stupid man,' as she referred to him. For years she continued to work full-time as a cashier in the accounts department before joining a small private firm owned and run by a female accountant.

By the time I am born, Grandad works part-time while Nan works full-time. This is an unusual arrangement in that era, but Grandad had his first heart attack at age forty-two.

He also suffers from a bad back. There are days and weeks when he can hardly walk. He often wears a back brace.

—

Grandad is especially close to my brother, Byron, who is four years older than me. Byron has dark hair, blue eyes and quiet ways. He is a Cub, Scout and then a Venturer. (We are all in the Scout and Girl Guide Movement – camping, sailing, rowing and bushwalking.) At school Byron loves woodwork and metalwork, and he loves to tinker with anything electrical or technical. He builds his first radio before he is ten years old. The garage is full of parts he's found and collected: circuit boards, radios, household devices, old business equipment. He spends hours wiring things, making small machines, listening to voices around the world. He builds an electric go-kart that carries him up the incline of our driveway. At fourteen, he hears a neighbour trying and failing to start his mower. He listens, then he says to Dad, 'I think I can help with that.' Off he goes and, a few minutes later, he's back. 'All sorted,' he says. He does odd jobs for neighbours and, at fifteen, buys himself a sailing dinghy to build from a kit.

They go away together on weekends, Byron, Nan and Grandad. The boat at the shack is called *Miss Wiggs*, a nickname Grandad gave my mother as a child. *Miss Wiggs* is a white clinker dinghy not much more than seven feet long, almost a coracle. We all learn to row in her with Grandad. Nan prefers to wait on the shore and read a book or go for a walk.

—

At the start of the winter school holidays, Nan and Grandad take Byron to the shack. The rest of us will follow in a few days. They decide to take *Miss Wiggs* on a trailer to Saltwater River on Lime Bay, half an hour away, to set a net. Early mornings there are breathtaking, the water the lucent lime of its name. There are ravens, sea eagles, gulls and shorebirds, sandstone rocks and ledges graced by she-oaks and gum trees. There are fish aplenty. Bays, inlets, rivers, swamps, lagoons and wetlands: they're best approached with a little local knowledge. Grandad knows the Tasman Peninsula like he knows how to clean a fish.

The day is serene and cloudless, and the net is set. Then a stiff breeze comes in. As Grandad and Byron retrieve the net, they fall out of the boat. One moment they are in the dinghy; the next it is an upturned hull and they are clinging to the side.

The water in Tasmania is very cold in August. It's particularly cold that far south, on the Tasman Peninsula. Nan sees the boat upturned, sees them in the water through the binoculars. She can't drive. At sixty, with arthritis, she runs for help. They are not far off shore and they are both good swimmers.

—

Back at home, Dad has gone to the shop. Mum is at work. I answer the door when the bell rings. It's a policeman. The river is shining behind him.

He says, 'Do you know Leonard Keith Burgess and Byron Kent Rose?'

'Yes,' I say. 'One's my grandfather and one's my brother.'

Something passes across his face. I am the same height then as I am now, and I look older than my twelve years. Perhaps he has realised I am not a teenager, and not the right person to ask, but it feels like something else. It feels like pain slices through him. He averts his face and asks, 'Is your mum or dad here?'

I explain that Dad will be back in a moment. I invite him to wait in the lounge room, but he says he'll wait in his car. When I close the door, my sister is standing behind me. She says, 'What did he want?'

'Byron and Grandad are dead,' I say.

My sister is almost nine. I see her register my words as I had registered the death of Pa Rose. It is a fact. She frowns. 'How do you know?' she asks.

'I just know,' I say.

I know because that morning I dreamed I was drowning. I was in the water with Grandad but I couldn't keep him afloat. He wanted me to let go but I wouldn't let go and nothing seemed to matter as long as I kept holding on. The sky was very blue. The water was in me and outside me. The sun and the water were light. I couldn't breathe. I wanted to breathe but there was only water filling my lungs. I was coming up for air, but there was no air, and I wasn't me, I was Byron. I had woken from this dream gasping, completely convinced that my brother was drowning. I wanted to run into my parents' bedroom and plead with them to drive down to the shack and help. But dreams are dreams. No one would believe me. I lay there and relived that dream over and over and did nothing. When I saw the policeman at the door, when he asked that question, I knew.

I made myself wrong for that for years. For not rousing my parents and convincing them to do something. For not saving them. For not saving Byron. I had waved goodbye to him from my bedroom window just the day before. As he waved back, I had seen a white light around him, as if he were glowing. I remember thinking, *Oh, I've never seen a white one like that before.* This suggests I'd seen colours around other people, but I have no recollection of that.

—

My dad and the policeman sit in the police car and then Dad comes inside. Mum is driven home from work by a colleague. Dad waits on the garden wall for her to arrive. As she comes up the path, she is wailing in the most indelible way. The media gets hold of it before my parents have time to tell friends, neighbours and relatives. It is on the news that night and the next day it is on the front page of the newspaper.

TWO DIE IN RIVER

A day's fishing for a grandfather and his grandson ended in tragedy yesterday when both drowned in the Saltwater River. Dead are Leonard Keith Burgess (66) of Howden and Byron Kent Rose (15) . . .

—

There is a memorial service at the cathedral in town. There are no coffins, just flowers, at my mother's request. She cannot bear to see the two coffins side by side. When the service ends and we stand to leave, I see that the church is packed with hundreds of Grandad's friends, Byron's friends, my parents' friends, school friends. Scouts, Guides, Rangers and Rovers, all in uniform, make a guard of honour with oars from our troop rowboats as my family walk back down the aisle to leave the church.

After the funeral, with a bag already packed, I am sent off to a week of Girl Guide camp. One evening a girl I don't know says, 'You're just being like that because your brother died.' I run into a storage room and lock the door. I howl in that small dark room. People bang on the door. I don't want to see anyone and I don't want anyone to see me. A leader with a kind voice eventually persuades me to unlock the door. The following day, I'm driven home. I walk into a silent house. No one is home. The lounge room is filled with vases of flowers smelling of decay.

I go to my room, lie on the bed and cry. Then I hear a noise and look up. Byron is standing in the open doorway. He is smiling his quiet, blue-eyed smile and he is a little bit transparent. He doesn't speak but I can hear his voice. He says, 'You don't need to be sad. I'm all right. Everything is all right.' We continue looking at each other, until he fades away. I feel a sense of peace and reassurance. Yes, Byron is dead, but wherever he is, he's fine. I don't need to worry. He's okay.

A few weeks later, I walk into the lounge room. There is Byron again, this time sitting in the chair by the bookshelf. Again, he is a bit transparent, and again he is smiling at me, reassuring me that he isn't far away, no matter how hard things get.

Years later, Dad and my remaining brother will tell me, on separate occasions, that they too saw Byron in the chair in the lounge room. They both believed he had come to check on them and reassure them.

—

My parents are not okay. My father is utterly bereft and my mother is an abyss of pain. I hear her say to my father one night, not long after the funeral, 'He wouldn't have died if you had loved him more.'

My mother lost her father and her son, the two people she loved most in all the world. My father lost his son and his wife. My siblings and I lost our brother, our grandfather and our family. No one knew what to do with each other. Grief turned us into wounded animals.

—

But death comes in numbers.

Our primary school has just one hundred students. In grade one, after the allocation of two children to each desk, I am the odd number out, so I get a desk to myself. I'm thrilled by this, but then a little blond-haired boy called Nicholas arrives halfway through the year and I am asked to move over. I am annoyed, but I acquiesce.

Nick and I discover that we live in the same cul-de-sac. We both love to read. We love song lyrics and poems. We begin walking to and from school together. Nick and his family speak with English accents like the people on the radio. They eat different food and, in all sorts of ways, they are fascinating and fun. Nick has two younger brothers, Tom and Giles.

Nick and I spend hours together. He teaches me chess and we immerse ourselves in strategy. On the lounge room floor, on his bed, wandering the beach or traversing the paddocks behind our houses, our conversations are a debate, an intense discussion, or an argument. We will disagree just for the fun of it. Everything is hilarious, curious, amazing or mysterious. Nick's dad and mine have tomato-growing competitions. Nick's mum and mine are fast friends, their laughter like bird calls at any gathering. Nick's dad puts mayonnaise in sandwiches – a taste revelation that awes me.

My family owns just a handful of books; everything else comes from the library. Nick's family have shelves of books. They have hardbacks of Enid Blyton's *The Adventurous Four*, and *Archie* and *Asterix* comics. They have the children's classics. Nick and I study their dictionary, their encyclopaedia, their atlas. In grade three, our teacher reads us *The Hobbit*. Nick and I become obsessed with it. From there we discover *The Lord of the Rings*. We save our pocket money and accumulate a shared collection of Enid Blyton's *Famous Five* novels.

In the year following Byron's death, Nick's dad builds us a Mirror, a three-metre racing dinghy with red sails. It is called *Raven*. Nick and I begin sailing together every Saturday and many Sundays, too.

One afternoon, Nick's youngest brother, Giles, strawberry blond and irrepressibly joyful, is scrambling about the cliffs above the beach with a bunch of friends. He falls and dies. He is nine years old. Our whole community is rocked. It is two and a half years after Byron's death.

Nick's family does grief very differently. They turn Giles's bedroom into a family room and put the television in there. Nick's mum talks about Giles. They are all allowed to talk about him and remember him, recount stories and things they all miss about him.

No one in my family ever mentions Byron's name. We do not talk about Grandad. No one talks about grief at all. There is a void at the heart of our home that nothing can repair. My remaining brother grows even harder to live with. He has always been mercurial. When he is happy, he can be charming and delightful, but when things don't go his way – a card game, a conversation, life – he is volatile. Now he sometimes becomes violent.

My sister becomes quieter and quieter, and stays close to Mum. Mum still cooks and works and does maternal things, but the joy has been knocked out of her. A bitterness sets in between my parents. There are silences at the dinner table, arguments, fights and long cold spells in which Mum and Dad do not speak to one another. I want everyone to be happy. If only I can make everyone happy, maybe it will be okay. Years later, when my own marriage unravels, I experience the same sense of defeat. I have failed to keep everyone happy.

—

Nick and I go on sailing together through our teenage years. Our fathers drive us all over the state to races and championships, *Raven* on the trailer behind us. I escape into books. I escape into words. I throw myself into sport. Along with sailing there is hockey, tennis, softball, netball, badminton, kayaking, running and, later, windsurfing. From age fourteen I work many jobs around my schooling – on the check-out at a big department store, at a health food store, as a gardener. I pick carnations and potatoes and babysit for neighbours. I am a Sea Ranger Guide. There are weekends away and community service.

For a little while, two Harley-riding Vietnam war veterans live next door, an anomaly in our quiet neighbourhood. One of them introduces me to the writings of the Beat generation. He plays the albums of Neil Young, Jimi Hendrix, Joni Mitchell and Janis Joplin. He dislikes my first boyfriend and he is right to, but it takes me a while to extricate myself from that relationship. He tells me to be kind to myself, to read ten new books each year, to keep writing. Their home is a brief and unlikely sanctuary in those turbulent years.

Our mother falls in love with another man. Dad moves to an apartment at her request. My brother does a stint in the navy but it doesn't work out. He moves to the west coast of Tasmania to labour on a hydro-electricity scheme. I bury myself in study, doing eleven subjects over two years, topping the state in drama. I smoke a fair bit of marijuana but I'm less interested in alcohol. I represent the state in debating, become a school ambassador and win various awards. Mum marries the other man and takes my sister to live with them in Hobart. By the end of year twelve, I'm living alone in the home where we were once a family.

After Christmas, I go to Queensland for a national sailing championship with Nick's family. I phone Mum while I am away and she tells me she's sold our house. When I get back, I have a week to move out.

Mum has found the love of her life, but her new husband finds ways to hurt and humiliate me and my siblings. He is clandestine and calculating, choosing his moments with care.

They rarely include us in their lives. In the years ahead, Mum will not come to my wedding, nor when my sons are born. I anguish over this for years. My brother and sister anguish, too, but we are not the children she wants to see.

Mum sells the shack when our children are young. We have not been invited there since she remarried. My siblings and I are keen to buy it together. When we propose this, Mum's husband tells her, 'You don't sell to family.' I think of getting a proxy, but I don't want Mum to have to deal with her husband when he finds out. So, the shack that Grandad built for us is sold.

A Seafarers' Memorial is created on the east coast of Tasmania. One plaque among many reads:

Leonard Keith Burgess and his grandson Byron Kent Rose drowned when their fishing dinghy overturned while recovering nets in a squall near Saltwater River 31.08.1976. Dearly loved by their family. Sadly missed.

Mum writes these words and attends the unveiling ceremony with her husband. She has *Miss Wiggs* burned. We learn of these things years afterwards.

—

Dad never embarks on another relationship. He retreats into monkish solitude. He plays the music he loves, he reads, he spends time with family and friends, gardens, walks and works until he retires at sixty after a triple bypass. He never stops loving our mother. When I lament her absence, he always gives me the same advice. 'Never forget, Heather, she had one terrible day, your mother. Never forget that.'

He asks me many times over the years: 'Have you called your mother?' He allows her to be the grief-stricken one. When I want to give up trying to maintain a connection, Dad urges me to continue to reach out, no matter how hard her husband makes it. 'With malice toward none, with charity for all . . .' he says, quoting his beloved Abraham Lincoln.

A few years back, Dad had a heart attack. After the triple bypass, he'd had a quadruple bypass too, plus eleven stents over twenty years, so I'd been anticipating this moment for a long time, dreading it, steeling myself for life without him. I call an ambulance, put a pillow under his head and kneel beside him. We are both thinking the same thing. *This is it.*

'Dad, is there anything you want to say?' I ask.

'I'm going to see my boy,' he replies.

It is the first time I understand the unspeakable pain he has carried all these years.

The ambulance arrives in record time. He doesn't die. He's eighty-seven now, in fragile health but endlessly optimistic, wise and generous. He is the great constant in all our lives, a treasured friend to his children and grandchildren. And I'm sure he's right. When he goes, my brother will be waiting for him.

—

When her husband died, some thirty years after they were married, Mum slowly came back into our lives. At his funeral, she said over and over to people there, with a note of surprise, 'I have such nice children. I have such nice children.' It was as if the love and care we had been able to give her through the weeks he was in hospital and following his death had woken her up to something she'd forgotten.

One day, a year or two after his death, she brings a delicious lunch from the local deli to my home. We sit out on the back deck. The sun is shining. Spring has come and the trees in the garden are in new leaf. It is a rare visit, a rare moment, yet it feels almost normal. Perhaps it is normal.

Birthdays and Christmases come around and we celebrate. We do not talk of the shack. We do not talk of the man our mother married. He's been dead quite a few years now. I may not have her in my life much longer. I take her flowers and keep her technology up to date. We talk of fun things, light things, easy things. She has become quite deaf and wears hearing aids. She has arthritis and is prone to spells of dizziness. Her body hurts her every day. She's a superb botanical artist, a watercolourist and miniaturist. She is still impeccably stylish. She still has a mischievous sense of humour. When I enrol at art school, she teaches me about mixing oil colours. Every day, she teaches me about love.

—

Nothing is solved. We go on and the scar tissue gets a little more pliable. It will never not be sad. It will never not hurt. It will go on being at the heart of my mother, my father, my brother, my sister and me. We are five of the millions and millions of people who walk this world carrying our grief in a knotted scarf and hoping it will not come undone.

Grief is a pilgrimage, a long song, a poem that is never quite finished. My brother Byron would be in his sixties now. Maybe a grandfather, living a life we can only imagine, bearded, still blue-eyed, still sailing and smiling, when in truth his bones lie under a pine tree overlooking the River Derwent.

———

The kit for the sailing dinghy that Byron didn't get to build was sold. Our parents distributed that small sum between my brother, my sister and me. I put it in a bank account and added to it with savings from my various jobs until I had enough money to leave Tasmania.

PRAYER

Stay close to anything that makes you glad you are alive.

HAFIZ

At eight years old I am mad about horses. I borrow every book I can find on my visits to the library with Dad. *Black Beauty, National Velvet, My Friend Flicka* . . .

My best girlfriend lives in the bush and she has a horse. My cousin has a horse. She lives on a farm in the country. I live on a regular block. At church I'm told that if you want God to hear you, then you pray, so I pray for a horse, but no horse arrives. I decide to get serious.

Every night between my ninth and tenth birthdays, I pray. I recite the same prayer over and over, zealously, passionately, fervently. 'Please, God, please, Jesus, please, please, please send me a horse for my tenth birthday.'

Mum organises horse camp for me during the holidays. I love the smell of horses. I love grooming them. I love their eyelashes and their faces, the feel of their coats under my hands, their colours and breeds and their names. I'm a little tentative about riding them, but over the week I become more confident. When I get home, I begin my pleas anew. Mum patiently reminds me that we have nowhere to keep a horse. I tell her real girls own horses. Real girls ride horses. She tells me she was mad about horses at my age, too. She assures me I'll grow out of it. I am certain I will not. I go on praying, night after night. 'Please God, please Jesus, please, please, please send me a horse for my tenth birthday.'

On the morning of my birthday, I throw back the curtains. There is no horse in the front yard. I check the backyard. No horse. The side yard. *No horse.*

Perhaps my horse is waiting at my friend's house? Maybe it's meant to be a surprise.

I go into the kitchen for breakfast. No horse is mentioned. When I call my friend, she says nothing about a new horse in their paddock.

How can God not have heard me? I had prayed *every day.* Was God listening? Was Jesus, who was meant to love little children, listening? I felt deceived. Maybe God wasn't even there. I'd had my doubts about heaven. I'd spent a lot of time lying on the grass and staring at clouds but I'd never glimpsed any castles or buildings, no faces in the sky or heavenly music, let alone a man with white hair looking down at me.

Out of Dad's hearing, Mum tells us that heaven is here on Earth. God is poppycock. Is she right? Can my atheist mother be right and my father wrong? What if there really is no one up there? No one listening?

I give God a few more weeks. I think maybe He'll show me in some other way that He has another plan for me and my horse. I wait. *Nothing happens.* I'm the girl who stood under a tree in the schoolyard and offered my life in service. What does it mean if I'm actually on my own down here? If we are all on our own?

———

The death of Byron and Grandad raises more questions. Where do we go when we die? I'd seen Byron's ghost in the doorway and in the chair. Were dead people really gone, or were they just invisible, mostly? How did time work?

At fourteen, I start writing a lot of existential poetry. Is life real or is it an illusion, some sort of dream? Am I an actor in everybody else's lives, or are they actors in mine? And if we are all acting, who is writing the play?

I become interested in witchcraft and the occult. I go to the library every week and nobody seems to notice what I borrow, so I begin reading books about witchcraft. I learn about spells and incantations. One night, I decide to hold a seance. My parents are out and my little sister is already asleep. I invite my brother who is also interested in the occult.

I close the curtains and my brother lights candles. I draw symbols in chalk on the dining room table, then I place a small drinking glass upside down in the centre of the table.

We sit opposite one another, breathe and settle. Then we put our forefingers lightly on the upturned glass. We've agreed to ask the spirit of our brother Byron to come and be with us. We'll ask only yes/no questions. *Yes* is to one side of the table; *no* is to the other. The room, the whole house, is very quiet.

The only light is from the candles. I call Byron to join us. We wait. My skin prickles. Is he here? I call again.

The glass shoots across the table, escaping our fingers, and almost tumbles onto the floor. We laugh skittishly, impressed but also startled. We confirm that neither of us used any force on the glass. It moved on its own.

We settle the glass again and once more put our fingers on its upturned base. I breathe. I ask if Byron is happy. If he is okay, wherever he is. This time the glass glides across the table. A *yes*. Is he in Heaven? A hesitation and then a *Yes*.

We are amazed. We don't know what else to ask, so I thank him for coming. We sit for a few moments unsure what to do next.

Emboldened, I decide to call in the spirits of the *Marie Celeste*. I've been fascinated by the disappearance of the crew on that ship in the Bermuda Triangle ever since I first read about it. What happened to them? We put our fingers on the glass. I ask the spirits from the *Marie Celeste* to join us.

For a few moments nothing happens. Then, beside me, a mist starts to form as if a winter fog is arriving in our dining room. There's a strange sound, too, like a heavy chain being pulled over rocks. It's suddenly cold. I am terrified. We are both terrified.

We run about yelling and screaming. My brother turns on all the lights. I sweep everything off the table, blowing out candles, obliterating chalk drawings. We bolt for our rooms at the end of the hallway. I pull the covers over my head and lie there, heart racing. I worry that I have called something into the house that might harm us.

It's not until I hear our parents return home that I'm able to relax. Byron had felt like a warm, familiar presence. The other thing had felt dark and immensely powerful.

A year or two later, at a Ranger Guide camp, some girls suggest we hold a seance in our bunk room. I counsel them against it but, when they are determined, I leave the room and find a bed elsewhere. I have never wanted to participate in a seance again.

—

At seventeen I meet Alastair. He has just returned to Tasmania after working as a professional sailor in Europe and the West Indies. He is twenty-one, drives an old Kingswood station wagon with his windsurfer strapped to the roof, and rides a Ducati 860 fast. Alastair's parents have been divorced for years. They are both spiritual people. His mother tells me about Findhorn in northern Scotland, the spiritual community co-founded by Eileen Caddy. I read Caddy's books. His father introduces me to the writing of Helena Blavatsky, founder of the Theosophical Society. I am curious about Buddhism. I read James Hilton's *Lost Horizon* about the mythical Shangri-La in Tibet and become a vegetarian.

I've been working full-time in the public service since finishing year twelve. I can't afford to go to university, so I'm saving up to go overseas. I want to go to Scotland. I also make cocktails at a new bar in town four nights a week, and I model through an agency. Alastair and I live together in a share house. He is studying for a Bachelor of Arts.

We go camping on remote beaches and windsurf in all weather. There are parties, a lot of sunshine, starry nights, fires and dancing. Alastair encourages me to go travelling. If we are meant to be together beyond this, he says, we will be. Armed with Peter Matthiessen's *The Snow Leopard* and a backpack, I depart Tasmania at the beginning of 1984.

HEAT

What does it take to be a traveller? It's finding
you know nothing, that you are completely naked,
completely vulnerable – and so you offer yourself.

ANTHONY WELLER

For a girl from Tasmania, Asia is another universe. I'd grown up on an island with half a million people. When I arrive in Indonesia in 1984, it has a population of 162 million. People co-habit with an intensity I can't understand, and it does something to their hearts. In the Hindu, Buddhist and Christian parts of the country, people are gracious to a fault. Despite their scant resources, they are hospitable, kind, warm and full of laughter. In Bali, members of different religions respect each other's feast days and celebrations. I love the generosity in that: the appreciation of there being many ways to live, love and connect with one another.

Ancient temples are adorned with tropical flowers. Small bowls of frangipani are at the door of my humble accommodation. Stone shrines along the roadway are festooned with vines of pink bougainvillaea. Carved deities and beads hang from the rear-view mirrors of cars and buses. People greet one another by joining their hands together as if in prayer and then bowing. Everyone rises at dawn to pray. Prayer is in the air, the food, the communion and cooperation of people living close together. The noises are bewitching, too. The frogs in the rice paddies. The breeze in the palm fronds. The marimba of insects, the dawn call of birds, the whispering of leafage. The light is soft, the air damp. The dawns are orange and the nights mauve. There is movement all around: farmers driving carts pulled by donkeys; cars tearing down an unsealed road half washed away by flood; buses overflowing with passengers balancing cabbages and children on their knees, chickens running in the aisles, birds in bamboo cages in the baggage racks. Dogs and cats frequent every alley, every roadside. There are birds, beetles and butterflies, moths and mosquitoes. Every living thing seems to be growing or dying with an urgency only the tropics demand. The dust, the clouds, the trees, the grasses, the rain banging on the tin roof – everything moves.

There are also canals rank with sewage, waste and decay. People live everywhere, from private haciendas behind high white walls to cardboard dwellings on open drains. There is rubbish everywhere, too. Plastic bags, broken containers, every kind of human detritus. Cars and motorbikes spew smoke. On every corner, people are waiting to cross roads thick with fumes. The open toilets and drains, the mangy dogs, the crazy traffic, the way being a white woman makes me stand out – it's all unfamiliar after Tasmania. Yet I love the kindness and happiness of the people. I love the warm air on my skin and the amazing food, the easy laughter of old women chewing betel nut, their warm hands that take mine asking me where I am from, do I have siblings, do I miss my home?

———

After travelling around Bali, I catch a boat to Java. It is my first experience of Islam. I dress modestly, wearing long sleeves and a long sarong. I've observed other Western women in skimpy tops and tight shorts, but I see the way the local women dress and I follow suit. I'm dark-haired and flat-chested, not the buxom, blonde Hollywood stereotype on the billboards for movies in the bigger towns. But this makes no difference. In Java the men seem to think every Western woman is there to be groped. I am touched, rubbed, squeezed, caressed, sneered at, leered at and spat at.

The poverty of Java wears me down. I watch a woman not much older than me drag her useless legs behind her as she slithers across a big dusty bus station. She hauls herself aboard our bus, pulling her crippled body down the aisle, through the animal faeces, spit, dirt and dust, her thin hand raised, asking for money, asking for help, past row after row of passengers, until she exits down the back stairs, dragging herself away to the next bus. Every day I see people begging. There are children with club feet, withered or missing limbs, conjunctivitis, tumours, burns, wounds and hacking coughs. Everywhere I look there is a relentlessness to life, each day an act of survival.

The homes of government ministers and military leaders stand behind high walls and guarded gates. Sprawling houses with manicured gardens and opulent fountains, servants and chauffeured cars can be glimpsed beyond. Yet the greater population must live with decay, disease and hunger. I cannot understand how humanity has come to this. What is the point of all this suffering? Why has it been allowed to get this bad? We have so much in the West; how could we tolerate other people living this way?

In Java I become ill. I can hardly get out of bed. I hear about an American doctor in the next village, so I go. I am the only Westerner waiting in the long queue through the heat of the day. When the doctor finally ushers me into the rudimentary clinic, I can tell he thinks I am yet another backpacker with a case of the runs. Can't I see there are people with real problems needing his attention? If he'd wanted clients like me, he could have stayed in Boston. He hands me a specimen jar and requests a stool sample. The jar I hand back is full of blood and stringy green mucus. His demeanour changes.

He has me lie down in a separate area. The test for typhoid will take a week, but in the meantime he will treat me for that. I tell him I'm on my way to Jakarta to catch a ship to Sumatra. He tells me I am not well enough to travel. I say I have to be. He gives me a large packet of antibiotics and tells me to come back and see him if I change my mind. He reminds me to check the poste restante in Jakarta for my test results before I leave on the ship to Sumatra. He tells me I shouldn't be going anywhere.

———

I am travelling with an Australian girl I met along the way. Aleisha is a tall, strong, honey-blonde force of nature with a wide, white smile. We take the bus to Jakarta together. I am too sick to get my mail. Aleisha organises us a twin bunk room on the ship. For the first time in months, I lie between crisp white sheets. I sleep and sleep. Arriving in Sumatra, I begin to feel better.

We head to Lake Toba in the north. The local community is small and Christian. Gone is the call to prayer at 4 am. Gone is the sense of being prey to the whims of men. We find two traditional Batak huts for rent. For a fortnight we swim, talk, read and listen to the silence as the reflection of the night sky twinkles in the pure inky lake. I feel as if I am recovering from whatever caused me to get so unwell.

After a couple of weeks, we leave the lake for Medan, Sumatra's capital city, to catch a flight to the island of Penang before we head north into Thailand. On the final leg of our journey, we are sitting at the back of the bus. Aleisha is by the window, and I am hemmed in by a group of young Indonesian men filling the rest of the back seat and several rows ahead. I am in a long sarong and a loose t-shirt. The young man next to me presses his leg against mine at every opportunity. Then he begins dropping coins onto the floor. He bends down and picks them up, putting his head against my leg as he does this, running his hand up my shin, joking with his friends. The group begin laughing and leering. Aleisha and I pretend we do not understand Indonesian. We stare out the window and do our best to ignore the situation. The closer we get to the city, the more sweltering the heat becomes and the worse the behaviour of the young men. Now it isn't just the one beside me. Others have turned around and are reaching out to touch us while we swat them off.

At the bus station, we emerge into the dusty chaos of tuk-tuks and becaks. We spring into the nearest becak and begin haggling over the fare to the airport. Suddenly we are surrounded by young men. One of them grabs my breasts, squeezing hard. I turn to see the young man who'd been beside me on the bus. He laughs, his friends, too. In a moment of blind anger, I clench my fist, pull back my arm and punch him in the face. His head reels back then jolts forward in an almost comic manner. I let fly with a second punch. This one knocks him to the ground, blood spurting from his nose. He does not get up. The men around him scream in horror and jump back from us. I turn to our driver and yell, 'Go! Go!' The becak leaps away.

It is only as we clear the gateway of the bus terminal that I turn to Aleisha. My very tall, very strong friend has been a reassuring presence these past weeks. Now her eyes are huge and her mouth wide open.

'That was the most surprising thing I've ever seen in my life,' she says.

She tells me that I've always seemed so calm through all sorts of difficulties and behaviours. Nothing seemed to faze me. So to see me knock a man flat in the dirt, maybe with a broken nose, was astonishing.

The becak driver begins calling out to people in the street. Locals wave and cheer. He explains that everyone is sick of the behaviour of those young men. I am still in shock, but as the adrenaline seeps away, I start laughing. Aleisha is laughing. Our driver is laughing. We laugh until tears roll down our faces.

I'd never learned to protect myself from attack. I'd never hit anyone. But knowing I had it in me, if it was required, was comforting as I continued on my travels.

OPIUM

*Only those who will risk going too far can
possibly find out how far one can go.*

T.S. ELIOT

Disembarking from the plane, I see a huge billboard which
reads: THE PENALTY FOR DRUG TRAFFICKING AND DRUG USE
IN MALAYSIA IS DEATH.

What a welcome, I think.

A few hours later, after we are settled into rooms in a
rambling colonial-era hotel that has seen far better days, another
backpacker asks me if I'd like to accompany them to an opium
den. I weigh this offer for a moment, in light of the airport
billboard, then accept.

After nightfall, I am hurrying down dark alleys under
corrugated-tin roofs, past dimly lit doorways and cats skulking
in the shadows, until we come to a low-ceilinged house squeezed
between small timber and tin homes. It has soft lighting and
gamelan music playing in the background. People lie about
on cushioned wooden lounges, tended by female assistants

in traditional garb offering pipes and tea. The clientele are all locals.

At first, the proprietor is wary of us Westerners. But soon, with money handed over and tea ordered, we too are lying on couches in the gloom. Shortly after, the delicious effect of poppy oil filters through my body and sweeps me away on its exotic sea.

I return to the opium den several times, despite the risk. Am I scared of ending up in a Malaysian jail? Does the death penalty worry me? I'm aware of the dangers, but I am keen to experience this ritual, this drug. Besides, I just don't think I'll get caught.

By day I discover the delights of Penang street food – curries, satays, custards and fruit juices. I tour the island and walk the beaches. I hang out with fellow travellers, drinking beers, sharing stories and swapping books for the road.

One of the travellers is a woman from Sydney with her nine-year-old son. He was born with only one leg and hops about the hotel and the streets like a sparrow. The Malaysian people are amazed by him. They cannot conceive that any child born in a wealthy nation might have challenges. He tells me that he is amazed to see other one-legged people begging on the street, a cup for donations placed in front of them.

'What would you do, if you lived here?' I ask him.

'I'd buy more cups,' he answers.

One night I awake to a chewing sound in my room. It's loud. *What* is chewing? And what is it chewing *on*? Like any wise traveller in Asia, I ignore it and go back to sleep. Sometimes, when I return to my room, I see a flash of black scuttle across the floor, disappearing under the wainscot. It's shiny but I am sure it doesn't have a tail. It can't be a rat or mouse, so I assume it's a cockroach. But a ten-centimetre cockroach?

The next night it wakes me again. The chewing is frenzied and determined.

When I pack to leave, I find a pair of my underpants under the bed. The crotch has been chewed right out of them.

———

Aleisha and I take a train, bus and then a ferry to the island of Koh Samui off the east coast of southern Thailand. We have heard it is beautiful and it doesn't disappoint. Traditional wooden huts line the palm-fringed white beaches, and there are no cars; bicycles and the odd motorbike are the only vehicles on the sandy pathways that link the small villages.

By the time we arrive, I'm feeling sick again. We rent two beachside huts barely big enough to stand up in. I am shaking and sweating. My teeth are chattering and every joint in my body hurts. I lie down and disappear into a grey fug.

For the next few days, I drift in and out of consciousness, racked with pain. I sense Aleisha coming and going, bringing water, sponging my forehead. I wake one night to see two dark figures standing at the foot of my bed. I'm not sure who they are. One of them asks, 'Do you think she'll die?'

The other replies, 'She might. Maybe.'

———

When I finally wake, the fever is gone, the pain is gone, and I am hungry. I emerge from the hut to find I am in paradise.

The sea is turquoise blue, the sand soft, the low surf warm and effervescent. I swim and eat and laugh again.

Life moves slowly on the lawns between the jungle and the beach. A few outdoor cafes offer tea, coconut water, beer, noodles, stir-fries, curries, whole baked fish, fried chicken, piquant salads. Westerners from all over the world are living here on very little money. It is uncrowded and peaceful.

Every Friday night a movie is shown on a projector. It's outdoors, the screen backed by a wall of jungle. One Friday, the film is Coppola's *Apocalypse Now.* We are all high on the excellent local marijuana. I watch Willard's mission and Kurtz's madness unfold while tropical life sweats and vibrates around me. It is surreal and horrifying.

Aleisha is keen to explore more of Thailand. I would like to stay on Koh Samui a little longer. So, we hug goodbye, grateful for the shared adventures. With her departure, for the first time I feel a long way from home.

Two German men live beside my hut in a wide, balconied bungalow complete with elegant furniture and regular deliveries of tea, food and other beverages. They have lived on Koh Samui for more than a year. From their chaises longues, they consume heroin, melting it in teaspoons and inhaling it as if it were the most normal thing in the world to do. From time to time, other travellers drop by: French, German, Dutch and English. It is like a European movie set of young people delighting in their tropical good fortune.

'If you are ever going to try it,' one of the Germans says to me, 'this is the place.' He indicates the azure sea, the cloudless sky. 'Here, it is so beautiful and the powder is pure. It is the one place in the world it is safe.'

I say yes.

—

Heroin takes all the noise away, all the pictures. It takes away judgement, pain, blame and shame. As a girl who lost her brother, her grandfather and her family in the horrible wash-up of chance, I can sink into an oblivion deeper than any sleep. I can obliterate all feeling. I can obliterate myself. There are no messy teenage stories in that oblivion. There is no past or future.

The afternoons become a spoon of white powder, a flame, and a long inhalation before dropping down, down, down into the abyss. At some point, I decide I want to find the people I love, so I go looking for death.

I glimpse it at first down dark corridors in my mind, but I turn back. When I finally let go, on a sweet balmy day, I slip down a long tunnel like an eel in water. The door to death, I discover, is old and mounted in the wall of a cave. The paint is black and worn, the latch made of weathered brass. Of course, I am hallucinating, but I don't know that then.

'Hello, Death,' I say. 'If I knock, will you answer? How easy it looks to be with you.'

The surface of the door is warm and dry. I feel the pull, the sweet release of letting everything go. I sense my body back in the hammock, but it is further and further away. Everything back up the tunnel is evaporating. Nothing matters. Ultimately nothing matters at all. Death is simply surrender. Death is freedom. All I have to do is push and the door will swing open.

Then a tiny voice says, 'No.' It says, 'Not this way. Not here. Go back. Go back. Not now.'

When I open my eyes, I am in the hammock. A warm breeze caresses my skin. Leaves are shifting on the palm trees, insect life is trilling and buzzing. In the distance I hear the sounds of people and domestic life. But, most of all, it is the light that welcomes me back. The golden light of the tropics swells about me. It is a symphony of a million colours catching on every surface – furniture, roof beams, jungle, ocean, sky, my arms. Glistening, sparkling, shimmering, reflecting, glowing.

'Hello, world,' I say.

That night at a cafe, I meet another German who has just arrived on the island. He is thirty years old and extremely thin, his skin pallid. His name is Fritz and he tells me that he and his travelling companion have just spent two months in a Bangkok jail. They were selling marijuana but it turned out their potential customer was an undercover policeman. Fritz is sanguine about the whole affair. At an outdoor table, we chat about life and books, history and the human experience. We are still sitting there talking, when the sun comes up the next morning. I feel inordinately happy to be alive.

I go back to my hut and pack my things. I buy a ticket for the boat to the mainland, and then I take a train. The following day, I arrive in Bangkok and I go in search of a monk called Chai.

LIGHT

I have always thirsted for knowledge, I have always been full of questions.

HERMANN HESSE

Chai's monastery is in the back streets of southern Bangkok. To get there, I take a longtail boat, hung with bright garlands of flowers, down the great Chao Phraya river. When you've grown up on the Derwent, other rivers feel modest in comparison, but the Chao Phraya is busier. Water taxis, launches and tourist boats make their way past elegant hotels, glass office towers, painted temples and floating markets. Houseboats are moored on the riverbanks and simple wooden homes balance on stilts at the river's edge. Children play, and washing sways in the warm air. Life is a littoral experience.

I alight at a wharf and make my way through increasingly narrow streets until I come to a gate through which I enter a courtyard. Wide stone floors and shady walkways lead to rooms and temples within the compound. It is a small monastery, not open to tourists or sightseers. Monks with alms bowls leave to walk the streets collecting offerings of money, food and gifts from the local community, as is the Buddhist way. Chimes announce the times for meditation and silence.

Chai has dark eyes in a kind, lopsided face. His head is shaved and he wears long saffron robes. He is thirty-three years old and has been a monk since he was twenty. He takes me to a low-ceilinged room where we sit on cushions on a wooden floor. A friend of mine met Chai in a Buddhist monastery in Perth when Chai was visiting there on a fellowship. He reads the letter of introduction that our mutual friend has written. He is delighted I've come to study Buddhism.

—

Every afternoon for two weeks, I travel down the river. Chai talks, I listen. I talk, he listens. I speak very little Thai and Chai's English is limited, but we manage. He is curious about my Western life. I am curious about his Buddhist life. His bright-eyed presence warms the room. We laugh at the gaps in what I understand of his life and he of mine. In his company, I feel lucky to exist. I feel lucky to be alive. Lucky to be in this place, with so much to learn.

Before I left Australia, someone told me that I would experience culture shock in Bangkok. I would find it polluted, crowded and intense, they said. But in truth, after Indonesia, every other country felt like a reprieve. Bangkok is a sprawling city with intense stretches of poverty beside pockets of extraordinary wealth. It is covered by a huge blanket of smog from the fumes of buses and cars, and the canals are polluted. But Buddhism is a soft breeze that seems to smooth human interactions amid the competition to survive. Whatever the West demands feels like the worst of this city.

I go with friends one night to Phat Phong Road and see the young girls on stage popping table tennis balls out of their vaginas, and much worse. I see the Western men, leery on cheap alcohol, groping girls who are barely pubescent, some clearly not, and taking them upstairs. I see the vacant eyes of the women, the flinching bodies, the surrender to that life because it is the only one on offer, the escape from poverty all but impossible.

In contrast, the monastery is a place of silent orange-garbed figures, the scent of incense, the sound of bare feet on flagstones. How far it all feels from the tumult of Bangkok on the other side of those high walls.

Chai suggests I further my studies at a monastery on the border of Laos. It was established by the head monk of Thailand so Westerners could study Buddhism and, if called, take vows to become a monk or a nun. I'd arrived in Bangkok near the beginning of the Rains Retreat, when monks and nuns go home to their villages to reconnect with family and community. Chai was heading to his village in the north of Thailand. I would go east.

———

The day I leave Bangkok, I wander the antique shops near the train station. In one dark store, crowded with furniture, I spy a small ivory figure on a glass shelf. It is a man reclining with a book upturned on his lap. He is laughing, as if he's just read something illuminating. I am enchanted. I buy him, wrap him in green felt, and carry him with me in my backpack for the next two years. Wherever I sleep, I will take him out. Home becomes that small carved figure and whatever book I am reading.

Years later I will read *The Hare with the Amber Eyes* by Edmund de Waal. It's a book about a collection of *netsuke*, small carved traditional Japanese ornaments worn on the sash of a kimono. When the author describes this collection, I pick up my little laughing man. He has two holes in his base. He is a *netsuke* who made his way to a shop in Bangkok and then to me. I have him still. He sits on a shelf of special things beside my writing desk.

—

The train to the border of Laos leaves Bangkok at 7 pm and will take about twelve hours. I settle in. I have dried beef strips, a few nuts, sticky rice, fruit and water. I have a slip of paper, too, on which Chai has written a note in decorative Thai script which looks nothing like the English alphabet. The first part of the note, he explained, is the station where I will alight. The second is the name of the monastery. He said I should show the note to someone at the station when I arrived, and they would help me. In Indonesia I picked up basic vocabulary quite fast, but the Thai language is a whole new level of complexity. This makes travelling into Thailand, far from anything familiar, feel precarious but also exhilarating. Laos is home to the remnant Khmer Rouge. It is 1984; the Vietnam War is not far in the past. Laos is considered the Wild West. I am heading towards it with only a scrap of paper to guide me.

I sleep a little on the way. There are many stops and many passengers coming and going, but the train is never crowded. I am the only Westerner.

Dawn breaks and a wide landscape of farmlands and low hills takes on colour and perspective. I scan the names of the stations we come to, comparing Chai's curly characters on paper to the script on the station walls. At last, there it is. A perfect match.

I grab my backpack and alight onto the platform. Outside, in the middle of a dusty roundabout, a rotund policeman stands on a concrete plinth directing buses and motorbikes. I dart across the road towards him and, putting my hands together in the Buddhist way, say, 'Sawasdee kha.' Good morning. I produce the slip of paper. The policeman studies it, studies me, and then grins. Indicating that I must stay put, he runs off. I slip my pack from my back and wait. I am tempted to continue directing the traffic.

After about five minutes, a motorbike veers towards me. It is being driven by the policeman. With great excitement, he indicates I should get on the back. I do, and he drives me through the town to a bus station. There he parks the bike and leads me to a bus. He speaks to the driver, who nods, greets me in the traditional way, and ushers me aboard. He refuses a bus fare and, when I offer money to the policeman for his efforts, he too shoos it away.

The bus is filled with women returning home from the early market, their baskets full of vegetables and assorted supplies. They call greetings and insist I sit with them. We drive out of town on an unpaved road. Passengers alight at villages and homes along the way. The bus empties out. In the distance, I see a stand of trees in the midst of acres of rice paddies. The bus halts and the driver indicates that this is my stop. The few remaining passengers wave as the bus pulls away.

I find myself staring up a long driveway. I suppose the monastery is here, wherever here is, but there is no-one in sight and no signage. As I walk towards the forest, I discover the driveway is longer than it looks, almost like a dream in which the destination keeps disappearing. When I reach the trees, the heat recedes. Sunlight streams through the forest canopy, making glades of dappled shadows. Walking paths create sandy veins leading away to a larger building in the distance. I see the roof of a great temple at the heart of the trees. The air rings with insect life.

A Western woman in a long black robe emerges from a dark-timbered two-storey building. We each put our hands together and bow, then she guides me inside, indicating I should leave my shoes at the door. Along a hallway she shows me which of the small rooms is to be mine. She departs briefly, and returns with a long loose black dress like hers and instructs me to put it on. She waits outside my room while I do this, then we walk together to the temple. We have not spoken a word.

The temple – or *sala*, as it is called – is built of polished wood with a wide lustrous floor. A great golden Buddha sits on a raised dais surrounded by fresh tropical flowers. The air in the temple glows in the morning light. The one meal of the day has just been served and eaten. Monks and nuns are dispersing back to their rooms. The village people who come every morning to prepare this meal offer me food and tea. Then I am taken to the Ajahn, the head monk, who explains the rules and schedule in a quiet voice using a minimum of words. Following that, I am immediately absorbed into a day of meditation – walking meditation, sitting meditation, chanting and more sitting meditation – until it is almost midnight.

At the end of that first day, I return to my room. A window looks out into the forest. It has flywire but no glass. The night is close and still. There is no electricity, so I light a candle. I spread my sleeping sheet on the narrow mattress. I sewed it from a single bedsheet before leaving Tasmania. By now, it's been washed so many times the cotton has softened and the yellow flowers have faded.

Turning to undress, I freeze. The candlelight has illuminated a mandala of huntsman spiders lurking on the flywire, each as big as my hand. I'm not worried by snakes. I don't mind heights. I don't mind fingernails on blackboards. But huntsmen send a chill through me: the size and colour and hairiness of them; the unpredictable way they run across ceilings and walls. I worry about them falling on me when I'm asleep. They were plentiful at the shack in Nubeena, their favourite haunt being the outdoor toilet. I never took a torch in there, causing Mum to laugh and say, 'You won't be able to see what you're doing.' I figured it was better to be ignorant than terrified.

I don't want to disturb anyone. I have no broom with which to shoo these spiders out. And even if I tried, they'd run in every direction. I can't take a shoe and whack them for the same reason. Besides, Buddhists believe in the sacredness of life. Killing is forbidden and I'm in a monastery. Even if I had the courage to pick them up and toss them outside, there are simply too many of them. Then one of them moves. With a huge sigh of relief, I see that they are on the outside of the flywire.

I slide into my sleeping sheet and rest my head on the pillow. Mosquitoes swirl about me but I am not allowed to kill them either. I sigh and raise my eyes to the ceiling. There, to my horror, are another twenty-three huntsmen awaiting their evening fare of small flying creatures. Twenty-three just above my head.

I am exhausted after my night on the train and the day I've just had. I stare at the spiders for a few minutes, then I blow out the candle and pull the sheet up over my head. Unlike a bed base filled with cockroaches that I discovered one night in Bali, I can't convince myself I haven't seen these spiders. Nothing will make them go away. Will they crawl over me in the night? Will they get inside my sheet?

I close my eyes and sleep.

Maybe the spiders do run over me. I don't know. At 3 am I am woken by the sound of a soft gong summoning us to the *sala*. The huntsmen are still there, watchful and silent, as I put on the black dress and depart for morning meditation.

—

Because it was established for Westerners, mostly Western monks and nuns live here. But, during the Rains Retreat, monks born in this area have come home, so we are a mixed group. In residence are fifteen monks, three nuns, a few male novices and three female guests, including me. The rules are simple: little talking, little eating and little sleeping.

Every morning large serving bowls are carried into the *sala* by the villagers. We sit cross-legged on low cushions around the edge of the room in order of seniority and the Ajahn offers prayers of gratitude. After that, silence prevails. Bowls are passed to the monks and then to the nuns. As the newest arrival, and a guest, I am at the end of the line. We each take what we want and place it in a bowl before us. Much of the food is unrecognisable and all of it is vegetarian. Mostly it is delicious. Some of the serving bowls are empty by the time they reach me. At the end of the line, you get what is left.

Watching that procession of dishes move towards me, the light sliding into the *sala* behind the monks, hearing the hushed footsteps of the villagers beyond, here is another world that goes on day after day. The chaotic, colourful world is out there — and here we are in an oasis of golden calm.

Knowing there is only one meal each day, I worry about the long days. Surely I'll be hungry. Observing the woman to my right, I see that, despite this being her only meal, she eats sparingly. I follow her example, and as the days become weeks, the idea of scarcity disappears.

I delight in everything that finds its way into my bowl. I delight in the morning rhythm that brings us here together, already hours into our day, drawn from our dawn contemplation to meet our physical needs. The silent reverence for the food, for the providers of the food, the quiet of the gathering, the humanity of the gathering, the intensity of the space watched over by the large Buddha, the way every item in the *sala* is shining and purposeful. The sense of the sacred in everything is nourishing.

After breakfast there are several hours of walking meditation, followed by more sitting meditation. For an hour or
so each afternoon, we undertake domestic tasks. We garden,
sweep the paths of fallen leaves and take care of basic upkeep.
The heavier gardening work and building jobs are undertaken
by the monks. After this we have private time for rest, then,
as early evening approaches, the gong rings and we return
to the *sala* for chanting and sitting meditation. The evening
meditations are lit by lanterns. Guidance is sometimes given on
a particular chant or Buddhist koan to reflect on in our practice. We finish around 11 pm then retreat through the darkness
to our beds. The gong sounds again at 3 am. Only on Sundays
does this rhythm change, when the head monk gives a talk in
the afternoon.

All in all, we meditate for thirteen to sixteen hours a day.
I have never been good at sitting cross-legged. My back aches,
my hips ache, but in the *sala* I learn to move in and out of the
pain. Some days are harder than others. Some hours are harder
than others. Sometimes it is the pure focus of breath after breath
just to remain sitting among my companions, meditating in
silence or chanting in unison. Sometimes the pain is a focusing
tool, like the breath.

Being in silence day after day is humbling, disorientating,
liberating, demanding, hard and sometimes very emotional.
We move about with respect and distance as we share our
daily rituals. We rarely make eye contact with one another.
Waves of loneliness, frustration, serenity, grief, shame, happiness, boredom, fatigue, yearning, bewilderment and love wash

through me. Emotions are like winds on the lake, the Buddhists say. You are the lake, peaceful and quiet. The winds come and go, ruffling the surface. They are erratic and temporary. The winds are not you. You are the lake.

I learn the impossibility of trying to use my brain to achieve a result in meditation. I learn the downward spiral of expectation, the uselessness of force and will, the yearning for connection with some greater force, the waiting for some sign that any of this means anything. I learn to surrender in minute increments, day after day, forcing my energetic nature to settle, corralling my need for distraction, subduing my urge to run, dance, laugh and talk. The external world is turned inwards so that the expanse of the breath and the texture of the mind become vibrant. Everything slows.

At times I glimpse the paradox of time and space. I sense the illusion of past and future. I glimpse the expanse of a universe in which this planet is just one small outpost of life. I am a speck on that outpost. I feel my identity becoming porous and sometimes it evaporates altogether. Then I come back to the heat and the ringing forest, the irritation and limitations of a busy mind and a restless body.

I find that words become strange to hear and slow to come to my mind. Sitting among these robed people with their shaved heads, I think about becoming a nun. I think about donning the grey robes of a female devotee and living here in this forest forever. How tranquil it might be, all a monastic life offers – the simplicity of rituals and patterns, the gong, the garden, the forest, the flow of breath, the silence.

—

One morning, as I am helping to prepare breakfast, I pick up a large metal bowl from a stack beneath a table and a huntsman falls out. The spider takes off up my leg under my long dress. I stay still. It runs up, up, up until it reaches my underpants. It freezes at the edge of the fabric, quivering. I can feel the terror in its body. I can sense its finely tuned nature and its overwhelm at living among enormous clumsy beings like me. Then it is away again, crossing my pubic bone and fleeing down my other leg, before racing back under the bench.

It has taken just a few moments and I have remained observant, without fear or alarm. I realise, from sensing its panic, that spiders are far more scared of us than we are of them. After that, while I'm still not comfortable with huntsmen, and I would prefer not to have them near me, they cease to terrify me. I am aware of their sentience and our shared urge to survive.

—

Long days and weeks of meditation do strange things to the brain. My dreams become long and complex. Flashes of memory are sometimes vividly colourful. I know I am thinner but there are no mirrors. One of the other guests shaves my head. I like the way this seems to open up my perception to a new radius of sensation. My hearing becomes more acute. In the few hours that we sleep, my body rests but my mind is alert. Sleep becomes an extension of meditation. A time of breath and release, a supine reprieve for the body.

My days are a pattern of wake, meditate, eat, meditate, walk, sit, chant, sweep the paths, observe the forest, rest on my bed, meditate, chant, breathe, sleep. I see the way my hand holds a bowl. I feel the wooden broom against my fingers, the sand on the path under my bare feet, the air moist on my face. I listen to soft rain on broad tropical leaves and birds waking before dawn. I observe stars through the canopy and rice fields beyond the forest. The fabric of my long black robe rustles as I walk. I am attuned to the forest and the distant sound of village life drifting through the trees on a certain breeze. My body has become a tuning fork for sensation. My mind, still often loud, quietens. Talking is forgotten.

Sometimes I feel as transparent as a shaft of sunshine between trees. Other times I feel slow, cumbersome, bound by gravity. It is weeks since I last wrote in my journal. I haven't read anything. I haven't talked to anyone. While I giggle silently to myself, amused by the clumsy moments of life, I haven't laughed with anyone. I haven't missed it. Solitude and silence are a well I love drinking from.

I sink into the idea that this is where I belong. I will stay here and become a Buddhist nun. Despite my love of people, conversation, friends, sex, the whole crazy spectrum of human experience, this serenity, these rhythms and rituals, it fulfils me. I want it to go on and never stop.

One afternoon, I am meditating in a small temple to one side of the forest where I am usually alone. On a dais, a human-sized golden Buddha sits cross-legged and smiling, adorned with fresh flowers. The walls of this *sala* are made of vertical slats of honeyed timber, spaced an inch apart so that fingers of sunlight slide through. The scent of incense lingers, mosquitoes swirl, the forest trembles.

I close my eyes and sink into my breath as I have done so many times before. I rest in that familiar darkness. And then something different happens. I seem to be on a dark hill. The view is remarkable. Before me are millions of lights – lights as bright as stars sparkling in an immense void. I understand that the lights are us, the beings are us. Each of us *is* a light. None of us is brighter or duller than another. Every one of us glows exactly the same. Each of us is beautiful beyond imagination.

I don't know how long I sit there in this bliss, a watcher without time or form.

When I open my eyes, a young Thai monk has entered the *sala* soundlessly. He is gazing at me. He bows and quietly retreats. I realise tears are running down my face.

We are all lights! I want to tell him. I am a light. He is a light. We are both bright and beautiful. No matter what form we take, whatever we do or do not do with our lives, we are each part of a timeless and infinite darkness that is alive with energy.

I begin to laugh. I laugh quietly at first and then, as emotion overwhelms me, I laugh aloud. I laugh until I have to lie down on the floor. I laugh as tears flow. I roll on the floor and laugh at the delight of it all. We attribute all this significance to our lives, yet we're light. Light. Every one of us is light.

To this day, my favourite Buddha is the laughing Buddha. He sits beside my little ivory man with his book. He reminds me that through all that life brings, this too is true: we are beautiful beyond imagining, every one of us. We are shining and eternal.

Meditation is a doorway. Meditation is a frequency. I am nineteen. From then on, I want to go back to the place with the lights and never leave. But the intensity of that one afternoon does not return, though I stay on in the monastery.

—

On Sunday afternoons, the senior monk shares his thoughts on Buddhist theology. It is also the day we are given hot chocolate. A single cup of a watery variety, but hot chocolate nevertheless, which we sip as we listen. I am especially fascinated by what people ask on Sundays. We live in silence, so I know nothing about the people here, monks, nuns or guests. There is no conversation to reveal where we are from, what has brought us here, how long we have been here, nor what is happening for us during this period of intense retreat.

One female guest spent a week crying. She cried achingly and silently. I passed her sobbing on the path. I saw her in whispered conversation with another female guest, the grief evident on her face and in her body. I never learned what saddened her, and then she left.

It is not unusual to see other travellers walk up the driveway, as I had, seeking the mysteries within. They are welcomed as I was. They immerse themselves in life here. I no longer sit on the last cushion at breakfast. Then they are gone again.

I suppose we all sought the monastery to fill a need. Perhaps that need was solitude or contemplation. Perhaps it was a way of escaping the past or avoiding the future. I don't know. But on Sunday afternoons, people unveiled themselves in the questions they asked.

On one particular afternoon, an older nun in her grey robes, her head shaved, asks: 'How do we know that what we do here makes any difference?'

The head monk nods slowly. He says, 'When we meditate, we are each like a drop of rain. The rain hits the surface of the lake and rings spread out and out. What you do here, what we create here in meditation, it ripples out around the whole world.'

The words 'the whole world' startle me. I imagine rings of energy rippling out from the monastery over the surrounding fields, the rice paddies, the road back to the town and, in the distance, the train track. I see these waves continuing to ripple all the way back to Bangkok. Having reached Bangkok, I remember other places. I see energy rippling over China, India, the Middle East and on towards Europe. I see the Mediterranean and Africa, Australia, North America, South America, the South Pole, the North Pole, the whole blue-green planet with its oceans and mountains, its cities and people. I'd completely forgotten the world beyond. My life has become the path beneath my bare feet, the clatter of bowls in the kitchen, the mosquitoes at night, the *sala*, the chanting, the silence, the soft solace of meditation, the cadence of breath.

A thought occurs to me. *That's where I'm meant to be. I'm meant to be out there.*

But how can I leave this place? I wonder. How can I go back out there after this?

Over the next few days, I observe the monastery more intensely. I see the lives of the monks and nuns and their small houses in the trees. I see the quiet labours of the villagers. I see the temples and flowers, the statues and devotion. I don't want to leave here. It is solace and beauty. It is quiet and still. It is immersion in a different kind of life. Yet I can feel my stay coming to an end.

I go to the head monk and explain how the nun's question and his answer has made me recall the world. 'I have things to do out there,' I say. 'I don't know what, but it's time.'

He says, very gently, 'You are always welcome to come back.'

—

So, though I'd imagined staying forever, I leave the forest monastery. I walk down the long driveway between the fields and catch the bus back to the train station. The owner of a small cafe serves me tea and curry, refusing my money because he can see I have come from the monastery and it is, he says, an honour to care for me.

The idea that I can suddenly eat whatever I want, whenever I want, that I can speak with people, that I can walk at a normal pace not at meditation pace, that I do not have to wake at 3 am and meditate or chant, that I can drink beer if I want, wear whatever I like, is overwhelming at first.

I think of retaining parts of monastery life – the morning meditation, the simplicity of one meal a day. I sense how hard it might be to hold on to any of it.

We are the sum of our parts. I am the sum of all my adventures and a body that has been strong, vibrant, fragile and vulnerable. I can say the same about my character. In Bangkok I am in the midst of millions of people again. I feel as if I've been on an intergalactic adventure and am only now returned to Earth. I see the light in people's eyes. I see their grace in adversity. The Buddhist temples glow with a love of history and theology, and with a love of humanity itself.

I cannot be a nun yet, I tell myself, maybe later. For now, I must move on. I have work to do in the world. Something is calling me.

BLOOD

*It is my hope that you continue in joy, remain firm
and confident, do your best, remain young.*

LETTER FROM MY DAD, 1985

I buy a plane ticket to Hong Kong and plan to travel as deep
and as far into China as I can go. I want to see what remote-
ness might be like in other places. I want to find the rare,
unfrequented places of the world. I want to go overland into
Tibet and find a monastery.

On the flight to Hong Kong, I run into a fellow traveller
from Koh Samui. He is Canadian and has been to Hong Kong
before. He knows a hostel high in a tower block in Kowloon. It
is a grubby building in which the noise of hundreds of people
in tiny apartments ricochets along the hallways, but I have my
own room and the bed linen is clean. Out the small dusty part
of the window not filled with the air conditioner, I can see
endless identical high-rises and washing hanging from clothes
lines on every balcony. The city stretches on and on into the
low grey sky. I wonder if I will ever find the quiet isolation of
the monastery again.

On my second day in Hong Kong, riding on a ferry across Victoria Harbour, the feverish sweats from Koh Samui return. I am shivering and shaking.

Hours later, the Canadian finds me in my room, a sodden mess with a raging fever. He takes me by taxi to Queen Elizabeth Hospital, where I will spend two weeks.

The diagnosis is malaria.

—

Malaria attacks come and go through the two years I spend in Europe. Meanwhile, I herd goats on a Greek island, pick grapes in France and wash dishes in a London hospital. I fall in love with a boy from South Africa and we travel together for a year. I plant a small forest on the hills above Loch Ness, work as a waitress and chambermaid in a five-star hotel high in the Swiss Alps and learn to ski. I am a youth hostel manager on the Isle of Skye through a summer when it only stops raining on two afternoons. In London I am a companion to a British colonel. I am also a companion to a former concert pianist in Surrey. She plays Mozart, Rachmaninov and Chopin for hours each day but can no longer remember her name or where she lives. She is a lady and her husband a lord. He teaches me about wine and opera and introduces me to the royal family on Christmas Day. I shake hands with the Queen, instead of curtseying, and laugh with the Queen Mother about our almost identical hats.

One night, gallivanting with friends in London, I swing on a chandelier and tweak something in my back. The next morning, I'm unable to walk. The pain in my hips and my spine is intense. It does not subside in the coming days. Any movement is excruciating. Unable to walk or work, I am forced to return to Australia.

—

Alastair has moved to Melbourne after finishing university in Tasmania. He meets me at the airport, helps me from the airline wheelchair into the car, and drives me to his home. We resume our relationship, picking up where we left off, as if it were the most natural thing to do. A few days later, to add to the physical pain, I have a malaria attack. It isn't severe – the fever and shakes subside within days – but the pain in my joints and limbs remains fierce and unrelenting. I am only able to get around using a walking stick.

Weeks later, I see a rheumatologist. He diagnoses a condition called ankylosing spondylitis, a form of inflammatory arthritis in which muscles and ligaments of the spine become so inflamed they restrict movement.

'As you grow older, the flares will worsen,' he informs me. 'They will stiffen the spine permanently. Given the severity of this flare, you'll be in a wheelchair by the time you're thirty.'

I listen to this prognosis, then I stand up and hobble out of his office. *That is not my future*, I vow to myself. *Being in a wheelchair is not going to be my life.*

His diagnosis is correct, however. I do have ankylosing spondylitis or AS. AS used to fuse the spine until people were bent almost double, but the invention of anti-inflammatories stopped that. Perhaps he intended his words as a wake-up call, a warning that I should care for my body. If so, it worked.

It is rare for women to get AS; at least, that was the medical view at the time. It's hereditary, though no-one in my family had ever been diagnosed with it. I will learn much later that both my parents carry the genetic marker for it. Grandad Burgess had flares that prevented him from walking. My dad and his brothers have related conditions. My mum and sister, too.

I'd had symptoms since my early teens. Despite suffering back pain, I'd loved being physically active: sailing, hockey, athletics, swimming, kayaking, walks and camping. When the pain was serious, doctors and physios proffered various opinions, but the pain went away eventually and normal life resumed. After the AS diagnosis, some doctors suggested that malaria had weakened my immune system, increasing the severity of the condition in my body.

After the rheumatologist gives me his prognosis, I set about doing everything I can to stay well. I discover that almost nothing is known about the disease in women. All the research has been conducted on men. I begin my own research on a subject of one: me.

From that day forward, I focus on health. I eat carefully, determining which foods increase pain. I exercise. I become devoted to Iyengar and Ashtanga yoga. Most evenings, no matter the weather, Alastair and I walk to the sea. I enrol in a TAFE course. One of the subjects I choose is novel-writing. I anticipate learning the theory of novel-writing, but no: over the coming year, we must write a novel. It seems a mammoth and ludicrous thing to attempt. I don't own a typewriter, nor do I know how to type, so I write that first novel longhand.

My writing is awkward, stilted and ignorant. I despair at how difficult creating a chapter turns out to be. After *The Old Man and the Sea,* Dad had introduced me to Lee, Steinbeck, Fitzgerald, Tolstoy, Dostoyevsky, Pasternak, Solzhenitsyn. In my teenage years I also read Austen, the Brontes, Michener, Heinlein, Brautigan, Robbins, Vonnegut. Overseas I consumed every good book I could find. Now I discover Faulkner, Hawthorne, Adams, Wharton . . . I know what good writing is – and mine is not that.

There is no depth of feeling, no sense of character, no wit or humour. There is only stilted dialogue, a loose plot and a vague sense of place. Despite my very best efforts, the late nights and endless drafts, and all the books I've read, my writing is terrible.

I express all this to my teacher, telling him I have to give up. He says, 'It's your first time. You can't expect to get it right. Don't let it defeat you. Just write it. There will be other novels after this one. Use it as a learning experience.'

After I finish the course, I fall into a job in advertising at one of the big firms in Melbourne, employed to write catalogues for a hardware chain. Sometimes I console myself by thinking that some two million people each week are finding my words in their letterbox. *Nylex garden hose, 30 metres, $7.99. Dulux Wash & Wear, 4 litres, $18.99. Kambrook kettle with 100 tea bags, $16.99.*

Two weeks into my time there, the senior copywriter calls me into his office. He is a small-framed man with gold-rimmed glasses. He says, 'Heather, what do you want to do with your life?'

'Write novels,' I reply.

'If that's what you really want, then I suggest you get on with it,' he says. 'It's easy to forget your dreams when you get into advertising. If that happens, your headstone is going to say: *Here lies Heather Rose, who wrote the great Coke commercial.*'

The first two weeks in that agency had been a heady mix of drinking, lunches and more drinking. After my colleague's words of advice, I refocused. By day I built my career as a copywriter. By night I wrote fiction. Within a few months, I was making my first TV commercial. I still wrote catalogues, but I was building a folio across TV, radio, press and print.

—

I tracked down that senior copywriter on social media a few years ago. He was still in advertising. I reminded him of his words and told him I'd written seven novels with my eighth about to be published. I said that without his advice, all those novels might not have emerged.

He wrote back: *Heather, I don't remember any of that.*

TIME

*Sometimes the only way to prevent losing
everything is to give everything up.*

JOURNAL, 1986

Alastair finds me in the kitchen eating gherkins from a
jar. I like gherkins but it is my second jar in a week. He
says, 'You're not pregnant, are you?'

I'd had a couple of operations that meant it would be almost
impossible for me to conceive. It didn't seem like a big deal.
I wanted to be a writer. Alastair's dream was to sail around the
world solo. When I was twelve I'd read the biography of aviator
and sailor Sir Francis Chichester, the first recorded person to
circumnavigate the world alone. I'd been to see his tiny boat
Gypsy Moth IV outside London. I imagined ocean from horizon
to horizon, the wind, the moon, the stars, the maps, sails and
solitude. It felt like a perfect life for a writer. Alastair and I
sailed together on other yachts through the racing season, but
he was keen to do a long voyage alone, taking a year or two
to sail around the planet. We collected boating magazines and

spent weekends driving around Melbourne and country Victoria, visiting marinas looking for the right yacht for him to buy.

But now I am pregnant.

Alastair is adamant that he doesn't want a child. I remind him this might be the only baby I'll ever have. It is a stalemate.

I am twenty-three. It feels young to have a baby. I've known Alastair since I was seventeen. I adore him. He is friend, guide, lover, dreamer – and he is a loner. He needs his own space and time.

I can feel in my bones that if I have this baby, I will end up as a single parent. Being a single parent is not the done thing. My parents will be unhappy about it. I'll be on my own financially, too. Maybe I'll have to go back to Tasmania. I don't want that.

Alastair is twenty-eight. We've looked at hundreds of yachts by now, but none has ever seemed quite right for him. Is sailing away from me his escape hatch in our relationship? I'd be happy to take the baby with us, but Alastair is hesitant about that idea.

Neither of us wants to marry. It hadn't looked good from what we'd seen of it. His parents and mine had both gone through acrimonious divorces.

I'm lost in a world of uncertainty but I'm going to have to make a decision. There is a person growing inside me.

—

Home is an old Californian bungalow we are renting in bayside Melbourne. An ancient apricot tree grows in the back-yard and we've made garden beds for zucchinis, tomatoes, pumpkins and spinach. The house is cold in winter and in summer jasmine grows through the slatted windows of the sunroom which is my office. Today it moves against the window shutter, clouds pass across the sky, a fly across the wall. I'm sitting at my desk and I cannot move. I am facing an enormous predicament. I feel desperately alone.

If this is the only baby I'll ever conceive, then I won't, I can't, let it go. I feel isolated and helpless in a body that has bewildered me but that might also be offering me a miracle. I sob with despair. Then something catches my attention.

I lift my head and listen. I can hear sweet music playing. But where is it coming from? I turn around, sensing a presence. Standing against the wall of the ramshackle office is a tall, dark-eyed, handsome man. He is not solid but he is extremely real. He is smiling at me with a warm, slow smile. He says, 'Mum, don't worry. It'll all be fine.'

I am stunned.

He smiles again. There is so much love in that smile. 'This is my time,' he says.

I'd seen my brother Byron twice after he died. But this wasn't a ghost.

A Swiss truck driver once rescued me from a snowbank where I'd fallen asleep in minus 25 degrees Celsius. I'd just escaped a near sexual assault. He took me to a diner and plied me with hot drinks and French fries until I revived, then navigated the narrow streets of Zurich in his sixteen-wheel Kenworth, ensuring I arrived at my destination safely. Throughout my life, people had appeared at vital moments, helping when I was all out of options, but those angels were real. Could an angel appear in the form of my future son?

I breathe slowly and nod.

'It will be fine,' he says again. 'It's my time.'

I wipe the tears from my cheeks as the apparition fades, his words resounding in my heart.

———

A couple of days later, Alastair and I visit our GP, John. John has seen me through the ankylosing diagnosis and through the last operation, which made my chances of ever getting pregnant so unlikely. He's given us his last appointment for the day so we can take as long as we need. Alastair explains he doesn't want to have a baby because he doesn't want the financial commitment. I say this might be my only chance. I feel like this baby wants to be born. I don't mention the apparition in my office. It is too weird.

John is a warm, kind Greek man with five daughters. He hears us both out. Then he looks at Alastair and tells him one of the most beautiful lies I've ever heard. He says, 'Alastair, babies don't cost anything.'

Of course, in a way he is right. Babies *can* sleep in a drawer, drink breastmilk and live in a sling. Beyond those first few months, however, it's a little different. Once they get to school, it becomes more expensive. But Alastair believes him.

At twenty weeks, I tell my direct report at the advertising agency. An hour later, our creative director, a man I am fond of, passes me in the corridor and says with a smile, 'I heard some news about you.'

'Yes,' I reply. 'I got a better job.'

———

In January 1989, a few minutes before midnight, Christopher is born. Labour is like the nature of the child I am about to birth: steady and reliable. Contractions come every three minutes. I feel as if I am floating on an undulating ocean. Every three minutes a giant wave comes in, picks me up and crashes me onto the rocks. After each wave, I struggle up, take another breath, and float again.

I had no idea it would be so painful, but also strangely blissful. There is an intelligence at work in my body. I am in awe. I had, until then, been pretty certain my brain ran everything. Not so, said the wise labouring body. Not so.

My obstetrician arrives. She observes me seated on the orange carpet of the birthing suite, my back against the bed. She observes my three-minute crashing-wave cycle. She examines me, noting I am five centimetres dilated five hours in. A textbook labour. She hands the midwife a script for pain relief. I am using rescue remedy – a homeopathic tincture – to subdue the pain, but now it occurs to me that it could stop altogether. The obstetrician leaves.

'Pain relief?' I ask.

The midwife looks at me, then she tears the script in two. She smiles and says, 'Back to work, dear Heather.' She runs a warm shower for me. She trusts that my body knows what to do. She offers me the chance to let it do its work uninterrupted and unimpeded, alert, awake and aware. She reassures me that this is what women do. This is one of the many things that makes us remarkable. I am strong, young and healthy. I can do it. I *am* doing it. The warm water of the shower washes over me. I breathe, crash and float on.

At the ten-hour mark, the midwife asks me if I need to push. The contractions have become a little faster.

'Yes,' I say.

I am on the floor. Alastair holds my left hand, the midwife my right. I have a vivid sense, as the pushing begins, of all the women from my family lines sitting behind me, sending the force of their love, their strength, reaching from the past and reassuring me. I almost dissolve with the sadness of my mother not being here with me. But another contraction comes and I am only my body.

One, two, three, four pushes and suddenly a whole new person slides out of me. A human! I've been so deep in labour, in the arms of my female ancestors, that I have forgotten the outcome. I look at the small being. 'It's a baby!' I say, shocked. 'It's a baby!'

The midwife and Alastair laugh. 'Yes,' says the midwife. 'It's a baby!'

—

He is six pounds with deep brown eyes and a thoughtful expression. He smells of caramel and vanilla, and I am in love with him. Christopher makes mothering easy. He is sweet, funny and entirely clear about his needs. Mostly he needs food and sleep. He loves to be cuddled, but he likes to sleep in his own room next to ours, not in our bed and not beside our bed. He likes his own space and his own quiet. He likes anything creative, fun or curious. He loves conversation. Long before he has English, we talk in the car, we talk in the bath, we talk as he sits in his high chair, we talk lying on the grass in the backyard. We live under the flight path to Moorabbin Airport. His first word, after 'Mumma' and 'Dadda', is 'plane'.

Six weeks after he is born, Alastair asks me when I am going back to work. Somehow, through the pregnancy, we have never discussed it. I am trying to find my feet in this new world of breastfeeding, interrupted sleep, a body changed by childbirth and a life that revolves around the needs of a tiny person. How can I give my baby to someone else to care for? I have no family in Melbourne. How can I leave him with strangers? Doesn't Christopher need this soft bubble of life at home, feeding, sleeping, the time to grow gently?

It breaks my heart that this bubble of mothering must burst. I hadn't considered that financial concerns about the future would take precedence. I want a simple life. I don't care about a fancy house, a fancy car, a fancy bank balance. I don't care about clothes or expensive restaurants. I'd never had any of that, and though I'd seen real wealth in England, the people hadn't seemed any happier. I want a garden, time to write, time with my baby, time to be a family.

Alastair is working for a big international company. He is very well paid with a car and generous annual bonuses. But when he was young, his father had acted the part of successful realtor while his family lived on nothing. Alastair has known genuine poverty. Financial security means everything to him.

He is a lovely dad, big, fun and gentle, delighted by his son. Riding on his shoulders is one of Christopher's favourite activities. Sleeping on Alastair's chest is a favourite place to rest. I want our little family to be okay.

So, I start a business working from home as a freelance copy-writer. I acquire clients and work around Christopher's routines, often staying up late to write, once he is settled for the night.

When Christopher turns one, I find a small childcare centre. He goes there for two short days a week while I attend presentations and meetings. I employ a nanny, Jenny, who cares for him for another two days a week. Jenny's presence at home means I can see Christopher throughout the day, walk to the park with him at lunchtime, and settle him for his afternoon nap. Jenny makes it possible for me to build a career around all the erratic and unpredictable requirements of parenting and advertising. Another mother, hearing me sing Jenny's praises, tells me that I must never let Christopher love her. It will confuse him, she says. But Jenny and Christopher do love one another and it is precious to see. She stays with us until Christopher starts primary school. The world needs more love, not less.

—

The years when mothering becomes the deep note, the wide curve, the drama and the comedy of my life, are full of magic. I know it isn't like that for some parents, but it is for me. There is that first year or two when sleep is unpredictable. There are breastfeeding problems, teething, colds and rashes, and more tiredness than I'd ever imagined. But to me mothering is the finest work on Earth. I am twenty-four. I have energy. I'm working. I'm a partner. I'm a friend. But first, I am someone's mother.

—

Chris will grow up to be tall, broad-shouldered and handsome like his dad. His dad comes from a long line of blue-eyed and blond-haired men, but Chris has dark hair, brown eyes and a warm, slow smile. He looks just like the man who spoke to me when I was eight weeks pregnant and told me it was his time. He's in San Francisco now, working in cryptocurrency. It is his time.

EARTH

Initiation is a passage from one place to another.
A doorway that once opened can never be closed.

MARK WAGNER

The rural forest outside Melbourne is hot and still, the creek dry and choked with weeds and willow. Suddenly I miss Tasmania acutely. I miss the grandeur of rainforest. I miss the towering gums, the vivid bursts of moss and fungi, flowers and ferns and the sound of a river wending its way through myrtle beech, sassafras, blackwood and leatherwood trees.

I am weary with the exhaustion that comes with parenting, partnering and building a career. I've been invited away on this weekend by a girlfriend who can see I need a break. I have no idea what I am in for, but I know I am desperate to be out of the city and camping under the stars. Even in a dry eucalyptus forest, being outside is my happy place.

We are a small group, just ten of us. The workshop leader is a wiry brown-skinned man with a beaded jacket and a long black braid. He is visiting from America. We are building a sweat lodge, a place of ritual purification.

We begin by cutting willow boughs in the creek bed and carrying them back to camp. These are bent and tied together into a low curved structure. Woollen blankets are laid over the willow frame until it is completely dark inside. Volcanic rocks are stacked on a wooden cradle in a large fire. Through the afternoon, the rocks heat until they are glowing. Meanwhile, we wrap pinches of tobacco in squares of red cloth and tie them with string, every pinch of tobacco a silent wish, a desire, a request, a prayer.

When I'd first come home from the UK, I'd made myself a meditation space in the spare room. My laughing Buddha sat on a low altar with a candle and flowers. When the ankylosing flare settled, and I could sit cross-legged again, I'd light the candle and meditate as the new day arrived.

In those early years in Melbourne, I often felt a deep sense of sadness. At first, I put it down to my overseas travels being cut short. Or the flat, concrete city I was now living in. Tasmania was just an hour's flight away, but I rarely went back. It was too painful. The distance between Mum and me, the hole that was once my family – it was raw. I was building a life away from there. My dad visited regularly; my sister, too. I had friends and colleagues. Still, there was an emptiness in me I didn't know how to fill. I surrendered to it only when I was alone, when Alastair was away sailing for the day, and then sometimes I cried for hours. It would have been easy to assume my relationship with Alastair was lacking, but in truth it was my relationship with myself.

After Christopher was born, the sadness disappeared. Meditation time was given to mothering, client deadlines and all the other demands of life. I practised yoga, took walks by the sea, wrote stories if I got the chance, and I delighted in the moment by moment of being a mum. Life left time for little else, and I missed connecting with the great unseen world I'd glimpsed during my time in the monastery. I'd come away on this weekend hoping it might ease that longing.

—

At dusk, I crawl inside a sweat lodge for the first time. The fire keeper slides the hot rocks into a central pit using a long-handled shovel. When the blankets come down over the doorway, we are enveloped in darkness illuminated only by the red heat of the rocks. The workshop leader, Earl, beats a drum and sings a Lakota song. He pours water from a ladle onto the stones. Steam envelops us, descending onto our heads in a searing blanket of heat. We are squeezed together, startled by the intensity of hot skin against hot skin, breath beside ragged breath, sweat instantly running from every pore. I am wrapped in a sarong and my shoulders are bare. My skin feels as if it is going to burn off. We whimper for relief, for the door to open, for the heat to abate, but the darkness and the heat, the beat of the drum, the Lakota songs, go on and on.

Four times the blankets at the door are pulled aside and the sweet respite of cool night air flows in. Four times hot stones are carried in and the blanket is lowered, darkness and heat returning. More songs are sung, prayers offered. The wet heat is almost intolerable, the earth beneath us damp with sweat.

Traditional ceremonies are created to challenge, to celebrate, to liberate, to empower. The sweat lodge is an invitation to pray for your life. It's hard, humbling, a reminder of your insignificance as a creature of Earth. Once it's all over, and you emerge at last, throwing your steaming body into a dam or creek or simply dropping onto cool earth, gulping water and night air, waiting for your heartbeat to settle, it's pure gratitude. But first, you have to sweat. Lodges can take hours. Some take all night. Time disappears. Only the breath, the heat and prayer remain.

—

When we are into the third round, I look across the lodge and I see two red eyes gazing back at me. I frown. They can't be real. They're not human. I close my eyes, thinking it is an apparition and will disappear. It does not. Those glowing eyes are vivid and insistent. Whether my own eyes are open or closed, they continue to observe me. It is extremely unsettling. I say nothing about this to anyone in the lodge as the ceremony continues, nor do I speak about it afterwards.

A few days later, when I am home again, I dream of two wolves with red-gold eyes appearing from out of the shadows of the forest and running towards the door of a small hut where I live. I slam the door shut and bolt it. They scratch and claw at the door. I do not let them in. The dream recurs over the following week. I go to visit the girlfriend who invited me away for the weekend. She is an older woman and wise in many things. I tell her about the dreams and the eyes I saw in the lodge. She says, 'Next time those wolves come to the door, let them in. Spirit is trying to give you a message.'

When the wolves return, I open the door. They leap across the hut and tear me apart. There is no pain or blood, just a feeling of complete disintegration. Only my right forearm remains. One of the wolves picks it up in her mouth and carries it as they cross hills and valleys until they enter a forest and come to a low fire. There my remains are placed onto the coals and burn away, becoming smoke rising into the night air.

A wolf speaks. 'Make prayer ties in red, five each night, until there are four hundred and five. We will be waiting for you.'

I have no idea what to make of this. I've had vivid dreams all my life, but this is vivid in a whole new way.

—

After that night, a new dream sequence begins. I am making prayer ties, beading leather, walking across pine needles in moccasined feet, listening to women sing songs. One old woman with a wide, bright-eyed face gives me similar instructions. *Make five red prayer ties every day for eighty-one days.* This dream occurs night after night, until I buy red fabric, a packet of Drum tobacco and a ball of string. Beginning this task feels like a fairy story. I don't know why I must undertake it. When I ask the old woman in my dreams, she says when they are made, I will know what to do.

When I wake from these dreams, I feel as if I have really travelled to those unfamiliar places. I can smell the fading scent of pine forest and smoke from the fire. I can feel the texture of beads against my fingers. Every night I make five red prayer ties. After a couple of weeks, I meet with Earl, the sweat lodge leader. I tell him about the dreams and my instructions – five red prayer ties for eighty-one days every day until there are 405.

'You're being called to a sun dance,' he says.

PIÑON

Whereas the sun dance is the time to pray for others,
the hanbleceya is the time to pray for yourself.

WHITE HEART

I have never heard of the sun dance. Other than what I had
learned on the sweat lodge weekend, I know nothing about
Native American ceremonial life. But across the Midwest, when
the choke cherries turn black, it is sun dance season. I go to
America and I leave Christopher at home. It is gut-wrenching,
mad, impulsive and utterly sane. The pull of whatever has
caught me up is evident, but Alastair is not happy about my
going. Spirituality is a challenge for him. I'll be away for four
weeks. My dad will come to stay for one of those weeks, and
Jenny, Christopher's nanny, will maintain schedules and rhythms
with Alastair.

Earl puts me in touch with people in San Francisco. They
welcome me into their community. They, too, have been called.
Recurrent dreams, strange messengers, a deep yearning, that's
how it happens. One evening, a sun dancer gifts me with a
Native American pipe that he has carved from soapstone. Every

person who seeks to sun dance must be a pipe carrier. To be a pipe carrier is to honour the Lakota ways, to be a servant of spirit, to help when called, to pay attention to the messages spirit sends. There is weight, responsibility and legacy in this. I hold the pipe, rest the long willow stem against my body and feel the curves of the red soapstone bowl. Then I fill it with the traditional herbs, light it and together with these new friends, I smoke my pipe for the first time.

To be accepted into a sun dance, I must first complete a vision quest, or *hanbleceya*. It is one of the seven sacred ceremonies of the Lakota. It's an initiation, like the sweat lodge, but tougher. Native Americans say three things can happen on vision quest. You may have a vision; you may go mad; or you may die.

I buy a 1974 brown Volvo in San Francisco for $200 and head to New Mexico. The land where the vision quest is to be held is rocky escarpments, canyons, sagebrush, sandy soil, high blue sky and high desert heat. It is June.

Eight of us will quest. We each walk the land alone to choose a site. I choose a high ledge looking down into a valley where I will be shaded by juniper and piñon trees. It is solitary and remote. I can see nothing of human habitation or activity.

As instructed, I mark out the site with long sticks driven into the earth, each bearing a flag. Red fabric for north, white for south, yellow for east, black for west. There are flags of blue for the sky and green for the earth, too. Then I return to camp for a final meal and to sleep before the ceremony begins at dawn. *Hanbleceya* – a Lakota word – means *crying for a vision*.

At dawn, fasting and silence begin. Those of us going up on the hill to vision quest enter a sweat lodge with the medicine man. After the lodge, I put on the dress I purchased back in San Francisco. It is long and tie-dyed. The woollen blanket I carry with me is a rainbow-patterned Pendleton. Someone tells me that spirit can't possibly miss me.

When I arrive at my site, I hang the prayer ties I have made – another 405 but this time in red, black, white, yellow, blue and green – between the flags. Here, inside the boundary of flags and ties, I am in ceremony. I make a mound of dirt, an altar, to rest my pipe on when I am not holding it. It is early and the sun is just above the line of forest. I breathe and sink into the morning, into the sounds and smells of nature under a sky of vivid, cloudless blue.

At the end of the first long day, dusk falls. Birds and insects perform their evening pastoral and the night deepens. It's amazing how long a day can feel without food or drink or conversation, when it is simply observed from a place of stillness. I haven't had such a day since I was in the monastery in Thailand seven years ago.

I am twenty-six now. I'm a mother. I'm very far from my little boy. The stakes feel high. I have come all this way, called by dreams to sun dance. I have been given a pipe, but am I worthy of it? Will I make it through the next three nights and days? Even if I make it through and complete this vital step, will I be allowed into a sun dance? Nothing is certain.

The moon comes up, and the sounds in the forest change. Stars appear, vivid overhead, and multiply until the night is a celestial baldachin. The task is to stay awake. I am hungry and thirsty and the night air is cold. In the desert, the temperature can drop from 35 degrees in daytime to 10 degrees at night. I must put all thoughts of discomfort aside.

I stand, holding my pipe. A pipe is a conduit to spirit, to keep me strong, to focus my prayers. It hasn't escaped me that for a person who turned her back on Christianity, who decided there was no 'God', I am now doing a lot of praying. My father has always been a beautiful role model in that. He exemplifies the best of his religion. Love, kindness and charity towards all.

I am seeking a vision. I am seeking answers. Why *am* I here? What do I need to know? What does spirit want of me, or for me?

I am taking my first steps on the red road, the path of spirit, the road of Native American rituals. Here, alone on a hill in New Mexico, I am following in the footsteps of countless others. I don't know where this red road is taking me, but it feels good and right.

Still, the first night is interminably long. The ground is hard beneath me. My mind summons strange fragments of dreams as I fend off sleep. I rouse myself, stand again, stare at the inky blackness, focus on stars and listen to the desert around me.

I pray for clarity. I pray for Christopher and Alastair. I pray to be allowed to sun dance, if it is what spirit wants of me. I watch the moon rise and slide past. I watch the world spinning through space. Scuttling noises emerge from the forest and pass by my site. I hear my breathing. I feel incredibly alone. What on Earth have I got myself into? I don't know if I can last. Maybe I can't do this. Maybe I don't have what it takes. I've made a mistake. I am soft and young and impulsive. I am thirsty. What was I thinking? Why had I come all this way?

Do I really believe in prayer? I don't like religion. Am I practising a religion?

But I know there is a greater force at work. The Lakota call that Wakan Tanka. The Great Spirit. The Great Unknown. The Great Mystery. This is what I sensed – the great mystery – under the eucalyptus tree when I was six years old. Was it the great mystery that called me all this way from Australia? Had it come to find me in a sweat lodge, sent me dreams and instructions, specific instructions that had taken me thousands of miles from a little boy I loved? If so, then why? Why am I so far away from everything dear and familiar to me? This is crazy. I wrap my blanket about me, lie on the sandy earth, curl my body around my pipe and I cry. What am I doing here?

Then I hear someone singing and drumming. A song is reaching out across the night from the base camp far down the valley. It is the voice of the medicine man keeping the sacred fire for us below. I don't know what words he is singing, but the sound of his voice, the sound of the drum in the night, reassures me. I take a deep breath and sit up. I hold my pipe, focus my mind and continue to pray. I pray for a vision that will show me the way. I pray for courage, strength and insight.

Several times over the nights and days that follow, the medicine man's drum and song come to me, rallying me through hunger and thirst, fatigue, dislocation, loneliness and fear. When I most need reassurance and strength, a song and a drum are there.

My brain wants food, tea, a gallon of water, a bed, a pillow, a roof, a campfire. It tells me that hunger, thirst, the rigour of standing still, the discipline of sitting still, the notion of staying awake, it is all ridiculous. Have I noticed there is a very high cliff just metres away? There are things out here that could bite me, kill me, eat me. During the day it is too hot, and at night it is too cold. Dehydration is dangerous. Why am I not worried about dying?

The hunger and thirst humbles and softens me. My thoughts are a noisy presence that I learn to silence because something else is awakening. A part of me that has lain dormant through the intensity of mothering, advertising and my relationship with Alastair. It is the part I left behind when I chose the world, when I chose this life over the life I might have lived if I'd become a Buddhist nun. I feel a quiet sense of belonging return. I am coming home to myself.

The second night becomes the third morning and the third morning becomes the third night. I am in love with the earth, the breeze, the ants and beetles, everything that passes across my site. I smell the scent of piñon trees. I see the moon surrender to the dawn and the sun subdue the day until the desert lies silent and watchful in the midday heat. I lose any sense of hunger or thirst. I am a watcher, an observer, a presence little different from the breeze that flows through the forest and ruffles the flags and ties. I have no sense of being other than nature. I am nature. By the time the last day unfurls, I am earth, trees, wind, sun and sky.

When I don't arrive back at base camp as instructed, helpers are dispatched. No-one knows exactly where my site is. The medicine man tells them to head up to the cliff in the distance. On my site, I become aware of a strange noise. The world looks clean and bright, new to my eyes as I gaze about. I feel as if I have been gone for hours into some other place. But where? I am sitting upright, holding my pipe. A moment ago, I was watching the sunrise, but now the sun is descending behind me. I feel as if I have entered a room I recently left to find the lights still on. And what is that noise?

Lumbering creatures appear in the forest. They are large and watery and they are making a strange call over and over. It puzzles me. What are these things? Then my brain clicks in. They are humans. People. But what is that noise they are making? They are calling something. They are calling, 'Heather! Heather! Heather!' At last, it falls into place. They are looking for me. They are calling my name.

—

Back at camp, I sit in the sweat lodge with the medicine man. We sweat and sing. He fills a ladle from the bucket of water used for dousing the stones, and I drink slowly and gratefully. He invites me to tell him all that has passed. When I am finished, he gifts me a spirit name. He says it will guide me all my life. A spirit name, like a spirit animal, is a private thing. I hadn't asked for it, nor had I expected it. But there will be many times ahead when my spirit name will have a bearing on my thinking. It is a beacon, a compass and always a reminder. I have shared it with only a handful of people.

At the feast that evening, those of us who quested are invited to share stories with those who stayed at camp and kept the fire burning, caring for life in our absence. Several people mention that when their despair was greatest, when they were losing strength and courage, the medicine man sang and drummed. We nod. We all heard it. But it becomes apparent that some of us heard it at dawn, others in the midday heat and some, like me, heard it during the night. Why was that? we ask. How many times had the medicine man sung and drummed for us? The supporters shake their heads. The medicine man smiles. No-one sang or drummed at all.

We are in disbelief. How could that be? The medicine man kept watch by the fire. The supporters brought him food and drink as he maintained his vigil, but he had sung no songs, there was no drum. He was silent the entire time we were away. What we'd heard, the medicine man explained, were spirit drums. Spirits helped each of us, singing and drumming, knowing just when each of us most needed assistance.

My Western brain has no way to understand this. But I'd lived it. I'd been the grateful recipient of spirit messages that had bolstered me when nothing else could. I couldn't dismiss it.

The medicine man tells us of another vision quest. This one was on the slopes of a mountain. One of the vision questers was a young man. On the third day, he heard an enormous noise crashing downhill towards him. In horror, he turned and saw a huge boulder rolling through the forest, knocking down saplings, crushing the undergrowth. He leaped off his site and watched as the boulder passed, taking with it his prayer flags and ties. Still holding his pipe, and terrified, he ran through the forest back to camp. When he got there, he told the medicine man what had happened, re-enacting the scene. The medicine man said they should take a walk back up the mountain to have a look. When they arrived, the site was untouched. The prayer ties and flags were in place. The forest was unharmed. There was no evidence of any disturbance.

This is Native American spirituality. The invisible, the inexplicable, the magical, it all gets close. I write in my journal: *I can hardly believe I am back in life. I feel as if part of me died up there with the trees and beetles, the sky and the earth. Part of me will never come down to the world here again.*

SMOKE

It takes a deep commitment to change and
an even deeper commitment to grow.

RALPH ELLISON

A Lakota medicine family from South Dakota is holding a sun dance in Oregon. I acquire travelling companions from the vision quest who are also headed to this dance. At altitude, in the mountains of New Mexico, Utah, Idaho and into Oregon, my $200 car breaks down on every uphill. On every uphill, one of us gets out, bangs the alternator with a spanner, and the Volvo goes on.

The sun dance ground is in a pine forest, hours from the nearest city. At the gate a big hand-painted sign specifies no cameras, no filming or recording, no drugs or alcohol. Imposing men with copper skin and dark braided hair, wearing check shirts and cowboy boots, assess everyone entering. They are AIM guys, members of the American Indian Movement started in the late 1960s to fight racism, poverty and police brutality.

Of the seven sacred ceremonies of the Lakota, I've participated in just two of them: *inipi* – the sweat lodge, the rite of purification; and *hanbleceya* – crying for a vision. There are also ceremonies for the making of relatives, a girl's coming of age, the throwing of the ball, the keeping of the soul. The most sacred Lakota ceremony of all is the *wiwang wacipi* – the sun dance.

I walk through the camp to present my pipe to the sun dance chief. He must assess whether I am worthy of this. The forest is quiet and scented, the ground underfoot soft with pine needles. It is just like the place I'd seen in my dreams when I'd been instructed to make prayer ties. I pass people preparing for the dance – women beading clothing, men dressing ropes and feathers, everyone making prayer ties.

The sun dance chief is sitting on a mat inside a large canvas teepee. He has a broad brown face and twinkling dark eyes. His grey hair is tied back in a braid and he is wearing a beaded denim jacket. I kneel and offer my pipe filled with the traditional herbs – bearberry, osha and red willow. He takes my pipe and holds it. He weighs it in his hands, silent, contemplative. Then he regards me. He asks me about my vision quest. He asks me about why I have come to this dance. He has been a sun dance chief for many years. He is also from a *yuwipi* family, I learn later. The *yuwipi* are healers and shamans. They walk the frequencies between this world and others, and they invite and chaperone the spirits in other realms to bring healing.

'You want to join this dance, huh?' he asks me.

'I do,' I say.

'You have to come back every year for four years. No matter how hard that is, you have to be willing to make that commitment. You have to come back to the tree and dance. Nothing can get in the way. Are you willing to commit to that?'

I nod. 'Yes.'

'You must live as a sun dancer for four years. That's a daily commitment. Every day you pray with this pipe of yours. Every day you live as a person of integrity, going where you're called to help. You have to live clean for four years – no drugs, no alcohol.'

I agree.

'Spirit has called you a long way. It's going to be hard. Are you ready for it to be hard?'

'I am,' I say.

'Well then,' he says, 'you can join this dance.'

He lights my pipe and we smoke it together.

—

The thing about commitment is we expect to succeed. Yet we fail. We fail all the time. We don't keep our word. We break our promises. We fail at relationships. We fail at marriages. We fall short of who we want to be. Sometimes we find a way to commit again. Sometimes we don't. Sometimes the obstacles to commitment are insurmountable. But this commitment, to return every year and sun dance, I know I can't fail at that. I will have to do whatever it takes.

SKIN

The bark of the tree can feel like human skin when you dance.

WHITE HEART

I'd been called into an ancient ritual on the other side of the world. The sun dance is a dance for life. For all that a human life is. People dance for courage, strength, healing, for loved ones, for forgiveness, for the wellbeing of family and tribe. What would carry me beyond hunger, thirst and physical exhaustion? What would my dance be?

Tasmanian forests filled my childhood with their scent, their sounds, their bright sparkling rivers and dramatic waterfalls. I'd been awed by wildlife, by bright-winged insects, trilling frogs, fish jumping, marsupials hopping and burrowing, and the morning, noon and evening cadence of birds. I'd been spellbound by the diversity of mosses, lichens, fungi, ferns, flowering plants and tree species observed on any walk.

In Scotland I'd worked planting a forest on the bare Scottish moors above Loch Ness. Those moors had been ancient forests before they'd been cleared for shipbuilding and sheep farming in the 1800s. Only small remnants of ancient forests still stood in England, France and Germany. While hitchhiking in Europe I'd been picked up by a scientist whose specialty was acid rain. He spent from Baden-Baden to Basel describing the impact it would have on our oceans, our drinking water and our ability to grow food. The Amazon rainforest – the lungs of the world – was being destroyed for large-scale agriculture and mining. There was growing concern about rising carbon in the atmosphere – the greenhouse effect.

When Christopher was born, the future of the world became tangible to me in a way it hadn't before. I wanted a world that was safe and healthy for my child. The next hundred years didn't look good.

Tasmania was powered by hydro-electricity, with more than fifty dams for power generation built through the twentieth century. In 1982 I'd turned eighteen and was eligible to vote in my first federal election. That year, it was announced that another dam was to be built in Tasmania on the beautiful Gordon River. That dam would impact the mighty and magnificent Franklin River that flowed from the mountains in the heart of Tasmania into the wild south-west. The fight that ensued between environmentalists and supporters of the dam gained international attention. The No Dams election put the first green politician into the Tasmanian parliament, the first elected green representative in the world.

My brother was working on an existing hydro dam at the time. He and his colleagues were told that if the Gordon wasn't dammed, their jobs would be lost. The Tasmanian government said that ten thousand jobs would be lost in all, a huge impact on the small population of Tasmania. My brother had mostly opted out of school. He wasn't the easiest person to employ.

Day after day, election advertising talked about job losses and the impact on people and communities across the island. I didn't want the Franklin to be destroyed but I also didn't want my brother to lose his job. I prevaricated until the moment I picked up the pencil to mark the ballot. Convinced by the government's claims about the economic impact, I voted to dam the Franklin River.

The federal government lost the election and the Franklin River was saved by the incoming Labor government. The dam did not go ahead. My brother did not lose his job. The jobs-and-growth story was a lie, trotted out endlessly by governments. Eventually my brother moved on to another job, and another. Tasmania continued to operate using the existing dams and has done so ever since, bringing wind power into the mix and selling green power to mainland Australia. The world did not end.

The Franklin River debate made Tasmania a drawcard for a new kind of tourist. Travellers wanting to connect with nature, experience wilderness, visit beautiful, rare and unpopulated places. Tasmania's tourism has centred on that ever since, making it a beloved international destination.

I was so ashamed of myself. What if my vote, and the vote of all those like me, *had* caused the damming of that magnificent river and the razing of countless hectares to make way for roads and infrastructure? How could I have been so gullible as to believe those claims? So self-centred? I lacked a long-term view. My vote was not only my vote. It was a vote for nature.

The Franklin didn't only belong to Tasmanians. Nor our forests. They belonged to the world. We were custodians.

I was sun dancing for Christopher, that he might have a good life. I was dancing for my ancestors and my descendants, in gratitude and blessing. But my other purpose, one I hadn't expected to find within me, was to dance for Tasmania's ancient forests, their extraordinary beauty and importance in our future. I wanted to dance for the trees that breathe for us and keep this world habitable. I didn't feel I could go back to live in Tasmania, but I could dance for it from afar.

—

Sun dance grounds vary in size depending on the dance. A field or clearing is chosen that is flat and smooth, and large enough to hold all the dancers. There is a shaded place for the drummers and singers on the dance ground perimeter. There are sweat lodges and teepees for the male and female dancers. The camp kitchen is placed away from the dance ground so food smells and chatter do not drift over the fasting dancers or the ceremony. A fire near the sweat lodges is kept burning throughout the four days of ceremony.

Everyone here is a helper, a supporter, a singer, a drummer, a cook, a fire keeper, a dancer. Everyone at camp makes this ceremony happen. The rules are strict. Dancers will dance from sun up to sun down. We will sweat in lodges morning and night. We will pray and sing and ignore the heat, the dehydration, the hunger and the fatigue.

—

At sunrise on the day the sun dance tree is to be felled, we gather beneath it. It is a cottonwood tree chosen for its size and the fork in its trunk. Its limbs are wide, its bright green leaves heart-shaped. The sun dance chief offers prayers and a young girl makes the first cut with a new axe. Each dancer hefts the axe and strikes a blow until the tree surrenders. Using ropes and pulleys, the tree is lowered, dancers and supporters taking the weight then carrying it to the dance ground. Stray leaves or twigs are all captured in tarpaulins held beneath the tree, then taken for burning in the fire that will heat rocks for our sweat lodges.

The tree is laid on rests in the centre of the dance ground. Male dancers wind their ropes around the tree. Prayer ties are wound around the trunk, too. I wrap the 405 ties I prepared back in Australia beside the ties of the other dancers. The branches of the tree are hung with long lengths of cotton fabric for the six directions – red for north; white for south; yellow for east; black for west; blue for sky; green for earth. When everything is ready, the tree is raised, its base secured in a deep hole. We all stand back. The tree, bedecked and emblazoned, is breathtaking. Sage is laid to mark the perimeter of the dance ground and now no-one but the sun dance chief and the dancers can enter this space.

The night before the dance begins, a final meal is shared before we dancers say farewell. I walk through the forest to the women's teepee. I take my dresses, moccasins, ceremonial items and the rainbow blanket that accompanied me through my vision quest. I'm not good at sewing, and I'd never seen a sun dance dress before I began, but I made my dresses by hand in the months before leaving Australia, guided by dreams. One is Guatemalan cotton in cream and black with blue and green ribbons. The other is plain calico with red and yellow ribbons.

In the women's teepee, I count eighteen women. Looking at their blanketed forms, I think of all that has brought them here. I have heard some of their stories – the cancer diagnosis of a loved one, a recovery from illness, the death of a child or partner, the seeking of a way forward, the chance to make amends, the yearning for a better future. We have all come a long way – physically, spiritually, emotionally.

I am one of the younger ones, but not the youngest. Some have danced many times. Some will complete their commitment this year. I am an unknown quantity in this ceremony. An Australian white woman just starting out. Untried. Untested.

The distant sounds of the camp beyond settle. I think of Christopher. I think of the days ahead. The heat, the thirst, or simply the ways in which spirit might undo me and I might falter and fail.

An almost-full moon has risen above the trees and the white canvas walls glow softly within. Our dresses, hanging above us, shift almost imperceptibly in the night air. I hear the quiet footsteps of a fire keeper and the crackling of wood as it is added to the fire.

Strange things have already happened in these days leading up to the dance. One morning, an older man was chopping wood. The head of the axe he was using broke off, flying fifty metres or more across the clearing in an arc so large and precise as to be impossible to replicate, striking the hand of a young man. It was a serious injury. People nodded when they saw the young man driven away to hospital in Portland, a four-hour drive.

'What happened?' I asked the lead sun dance woman, a Lakota woman from the Pine Ridge Reservation in South Dakota. She said the young man had been boasting about becoming a sun dancer, bragging of how he was going to tie buffalo skulls to his back and then maybe he'd hang from the tree, too.

'Not everyone makes it through the dance,' she said. 'Lots will drop. You watch. And some never enter the circle. They don't get that far. Spirit sends them away, so they can learn. Maybe next year they dance. Maybe next year they're ready. These ways are powerful. You don't mess with them. The spirits are watching. You're not out there to be the toughest. It's not a show of strength. It's about surrender. It's about giving everything. Young men find that especially hard.'

The young man did not return to the dance that year.

Two days before the dance, I was walking through the camp when I felt something sting my thigh. I instinctively grabbed it through the fabric of my long skirt, squeezing it tight, then releasing it. I saw the body of a wasp drop to the ground at my feet. I wanted to tell the woman walking beside me but my throat was tightening, my chest too. A group of people were gathered on the path ahead of me. Everything was breaking into pieces. I was clawing for air but I couldn't breathe. A woman stepped in front of me.

'Were you stung by a wasp?' she asked.

I nodded but the blackness closed in.

I woke in the sun dance chief's teepee, lying on rugs. The woman was placing homeopathic pills under my tongue. As the little white pills dissolved, my chest relaxed and I gulped air. People were gathered around me, looking concerned. Slowly my breathing steadied, my face and limbs stopped tingling.

'You had an anaphylactic reaction,' the woman said. 'Have you ever had a wasp bite before?'

I shook my head. 'Not in America.'

'My husband is allergic so I always have Apis on hand,' she said, rattling the bottle. 'I could see it happening to you. It can get worse, if you're bitten again. These little pills have saved his life several times. Take them. I have more. You must carry them with you.'

'Thank you,' I said.

'You were very lucky,' said another woman. 'You'd never have made it to hospital for a shot of adrenaline.'

'Someone is looking out for you,' sun dance chief added. 'You came a long way for this dance. Someone wants you to get through.'

—

I awake from incoherent dreams. Women are moving about in the dark, putting on the cotton shifts we wear in the sweat lodge. I do the same, and soon I'm standing beside the fire gazing at the rocks heating within the flames. Then I am crawling inside the lodge, into the darkness, squeezing in, shoulder to shoulder, hip to hip, with the women I will dance with. The air is filled with anticipation.

The senior woman dancer leads the lodge. A sage switch replaces the ladle in the water bucket, diminishing the temptation to drink. Hot rocks are carried in and the blanket over the entrance is lowered. The rocks are flicked with water. The steam envelops us, scalding and insistent. We sing the lodge songs. We offer our prayers for this day, for this dance. We breathe the sage-scented air. The blanket is pulled aside and more rocks are delivered, more water is flicked on the rocks, the heat increases, we sing and pray. Sweat pours from my skin. Four rounds of rocks, four rounds of prayers and songs. An hour or so later, we crawl back out into the world, steaming in the morning air, humbled, muted. Dawn is stirring the sky. We return to the teepee and dress in silence, helping one another to arrange the wreaths of fresh sage we wear on our heads. We pick up our fans, made from the feathers of birds that have significance for us. Here we go.

We line up outside the dance circle and the men line up beside us. They are bare-chested, each of them wearing a long length of red woollen fabric fixed like a sarong around the waist. Their wreaths of fresh sage each have two eagle feathers, antennas for spirit. Around their necks, on a length of leather, each man has a whistle made from the wing bone of an eagle. In our arms, we all carry our pipes filled with sacred herbs. We are a collective, united in a vision for a good dance.

Mist is snaking through the trees. Though it is dawn and the sky is lightening, the sun has yet to crest the peak behind us. The forest is chiaroscuro and the air is chilled.

I wait to enter the sun dance ground for the first time. The tree waits, the prayer flags in its high branches move gently.

The sun dance chief is among us now, standing by the altar. The drum begins, a huge ceremonial drum, beaten by men and women drumming in unison. Their voices ring out across the dance ground, rising into the sky. It is the first sun dance song I've ever heard and the hair on my arms lifts. I can feel my heartbeat. I place my pipe on the altar when it is my turn, and when all our pipes are laid out, the sun dance chief leads us into the arbour.

Now we are dancing. I have stepped back in time, or stepped sideways into another time altogether. I am in ceremonial clothing, in a sage crown, high in the hills of Oregon under a cottonwood tree wrapped in prayers. The earth is cold and I am glad of the moccasins on my feet.

The sun rises over the ridge and warms my face. We dance, lifting our feet up and down, up and down. The sun continues to climb into the immaculate blueness and the heat increases. The morning is measured by the arc of the sun, the beating of the drum. Supporters stand at the sage perimeter. Some also dance and sing, raising their arms as we do at the moments in the song where we call to great spirit. Some are still, sentries and witnesses. We all pray. Our prayers go wherever prayers go, into the sky, into the earth, into our bodies, into the past or future, travelling with our hearts. We dance in an amphitheatre of forest reverberating with song.

As dancers we are seeking a vision, waiting for guidance for the prayers we have offered. Our feet move. We stare into the sun. It is hot now. The muscles in my shoulders and neck ache as I lift my arms over and over again, saluting great spirit. Thirst whispers to me first, then hunger. We take a short break. We find shade and sit in silence. No-one can approach us. Then we are back within the circle, dancing, raising our arms in prayer.

A male dancer goes to the tree and lies down on the buffalo rug. The sun dance chief takes a scalpel and slides it into the dancer's skin on either side of his chest. Through each wound, he pushes a length of bone. Then the dancer's rope is unfurled from around the tree and tied to these bones. The dancer jumps up and walks back until the rope is tight between his flesh and the tree. He dances, leaning back, his eyes looking up at the tree, at the sky, into the sun. The skin on his chest stretches almost to breaking point. He is held by the tree, fastened to this conduit of spirit until flesh and spirit lets him go. Other male dancers do this as the day goes on. More will do it tomorrow and the next day, until the dance is done. Many of them are already scarred, their chests and backs a tapestry of prayers woven into flesh. Some will stay this way for all four days of the dance, attached to the tree, sleeping beneath its leafy boughs, their wounds open to the stars.

Skin stretches more than seems possible. Sometimes breaking comes easy, sometimes it's hard. Sometimes it's a matter of how deep a man is pierced through his chest, and sometimes it is about what needs to be released.

As the afternoon goes on, I see skin break, ropes ricochet, dancers stumble and sometimes fall, thudding onto the dry grass of the dance ground. Long moments pass. Sometimes the dancer is unconscious. No-one is allowed to touch him in this moment. He is having a vision. We dance on, sing louder, lift our arms to spirit and pray as one for his return.

The grass beneath our feet dries and withers in the heat, insects and birds fall silent. The drum, the songs, the dance goes on. Again, we are allowed a short break. We exit the arbour in a long line and settle wordlessly in the nearby shade. Then the drum calls us back. It is day one. We pray. We dance. The sun passes over and falls away. Only then is the last song sung. Only then do we file out of the sage circle and crawl back into the sweat lodge. We have been dancing for fourteen hours.

We are at the beginning of the road leading from the known into the unknown. We humans believe we are not supposed to be out in the heat all day. There's medical evidence to support this. We're not meant to enter very hot sweat lodges at dawn, then dance through a summer day with no food or water, then sweat again, steam scorching our sunburned skin, before we sleep. We are not meant to stare into the sun for hours. Still, this is what we do.

At last, back in the teepee, I lie down. I close my eyes and images of the day unfurl. My limbs are weary but my mind is beginning to travel. I see that it's not possible to dance by strength and endurance alone. It takes something else. It takes letting go of the known, the familiar. Through the night my stomach gurgles with hunger. My mouth and throat are parched. I wake often, trying to swallow, returning to fitful dreams of watermelon, bakeries, mountain rivers and water, always water.

—

Most of the people here are Indigenous Americans. Lakota (Sioux) were once nomadic warriors, moving across the plains of North America and into the Rocky Mountains according to the seasons. They fought the white man, fought him at every turn, but were outnumbered, outgunned, massacred and decimated by our diseases. The American government forced them onto reservations in North and South Dakota in the mid-1800s, harsh unforgiving land brutally cold in winter and searing hot in summer. It was designed to eliminate them, but it didn't.

When Lakota first encountered white people, back in the 1700s, they watched us hunt and shoot buffalo, taking only the best meat and leaving the rest to rot. We killed far more food than could be eaten. We killed mothers and calves, giving no thought to the health of the herd for another season. Eventually the herds that had sustained generations of Lakota were all but destroyed. In Lakota tradition, the buffalo is sacred. Everything is used, nothing wasted. Meat, skin, bone, sinew, every morsel is applied to life and living. The practices of white people earned us the name of *wasichu* – 'fat stealers'. We didn't just take the best of the buffalo meat; we took the best of the land, the best of everything the Earth provided, and we left behind destruction and waste.

There is nothing romantic about life on a reservation. I'd visit many over the coming years and always there was alcohol and drug abuse, domestic violence, sexual violence and just plain violence. Poverty, alcoholism and poor nutrition were pervasive. Late into the twentieth century, Lakota children were taken from their families, put into boarding schools, punished for speaking their own language, abused in all the ways imaginable for a child alone and far from home. Lakota were banned from performing the ceremonies that connected them to their spirits and their ancestors. So they practised them in secret.

It was the same for Indigenous people across North America. Despite the suffering and unspeakable loss of their lands and ways, they carried forward language, rituals and initiations to honour life. The sun dance has only been conducted without threat of white law since the 1970s.

The sun dance chief allowed people of other backgrounds to join this dance because he shared in a vision. Not red or white, black and yellow, but a brown people, commingled, intertwined, dancing together, one people upon the Earth. He wanted us to know these ways so that we, too, might learn the dance of spirit and place, human and creature, gift and responsibility.

—

By the second day of the dance, curious things start to happen. The songs hold me, the drumbeat carries me. Pierced men pull back against the tree, their skin stretching, eyes shining. A dancer who was wearing a bearskin cloak yesterday has disappeared and there is a bear dancing now across the circle. I am witnessing a real shapeshifter. It is unsettling and incredible.

I feel the forest listening to the songs and the drum. I don't understand all the Lakota words yet, but I'm learning. We are singing to the great mystery that binds us together, that shapes how we experience life. The tree, the dancers, the drummers and singers, the sun dance chief, the supporters, the pipes, the buffalo skull on the altar, the sun, moon and forest, it is all connected.

A rattle shakes behind me, and now above me. There is no-one there to shake the rattle, but I feel a presence and the sound enervates me. Birds fly through the dance ground. They cannot be real but I feel the passing of their wings. A cool breeze flows between the dancers, though not a leaf is moving on the sun dance tree. I am dancing into another world. It exists beyond the limitations of thinking, accessible through ritual, through the precision of ceremony. It is a powerful world, and its doorway is deprivation, hardship, commitment, suffering and love.

Mitakuye oyasin is a Lakota blessing. It is spoken at the end of prayers, as an acknowledgement of completion, but it is also a prayer in itself. It means 'we are all related'. Now I know why this is a prayer. I feel the connections between all things — nature, elements, atoms, energy, past, future, here and now. We are a great connected whole.

—

I dance through the days and I dream through the nights. In one dream I hold my head under a fountain in a village square and gulp water. In another I stick a straw into a hole, tapping a tributary beneath the teepee. In the morning I wake. I go to sweat and pray with the other women. The light returns and we dress for the dance. The sun dance chief leads us into the circle. The sun is behind the hill, behind the trees, and we wait for its warmth. The sun appears, rises, passes overhead. Round after round, song after song, prayer upon prayer, the world is golden, everything is golden, and then the day evaporates into twilight and is gone.

Each day, with each dance step, I pray for the trees. I pray for my island home. I pray for my family. I pray for Christopher and I miss him. I miss being with him to say goodnight. I miss reading him stories while he sits on my lap. I miss cooking his meals and pushing trucks along the floor. I miss painting with him and playing cars, trains, Lego and Play-Doh. I miss singing songs, lying under trees, wandering the beach with the breeze in our faces. I miss hugs in the morning and his soft breath on the pillow at night. I miss the smell of him.

Every night before sleep, I whisper, 'I love you. The world is so wonderful because you are here.'

It is painful to go without food and water for four days, to be sweated day and night in the summer heat. Yet it feels like a homecoming, this first dance. It doesn't feel strange. It feels familiar. Through the four days of the dance, every step is a prayer. The light is a blessing. The earth is a spirit. The sky is a promise. We start with seventy dancers and by the fourth day there are far fewer. Some people choose to dance for only one day or two. Some intend to dance the four days but cannot. Mind, body or spirit – something gives out. Still, I am surprised when I look about on the last day and see how few of us remain.

In the Western world, such a thing seems impossible: this heat, this lack of water, this dancing day after day. Surely our kidneys will give out, we will be blinded. But that doesn't happen. Instead, I become stronger in the arbour. The more my body surrenders to the sense that something else is carrying me through this dance, the more alive I feel.

—

Early on the fourth day, with the ground still cold beneath my feet, I go to the tree. The sun dance chief pierces my upper arms with a scalpel. He threads sinew and hangs an eagle feather from the wound in each arm. I dance this way, the feathers swinging through the day. It feels as if beams of light are shining out of the holes in my arms.

A dancer is pierced through his chest then pulled up by his rope through the fork in the cottonwood tree. His bare feet dangle several feet above the ground. The skin on his chest stretches from his body like fabric. His head falls back. His skin stretches more, but it does not tear. Everything stills — forest, insect, bird. We sing, our feet beat the dance, the drum chants time. We are asking spirit to hear this man's prayers.

The man pulls his body up the rope, hand over hand. When he drops, his weight snaps his skin but again it does not break. He pulls himself up again and drops for a third time. His body swings against the tree but his skin does not break and he does not fall. We sing harder, we dance harder, we pray harder. We watch, included in this suffering, moved by a fellow dancer giving himself in this way.

The air is ringing with heat. The dancer's arms beat as wings. He pulls himself up the rope a fourth time and drops again. This time his skin breaks, the tree lets him go, and he falls, landing as lightly as an elf. He lifts his arms in a wild salute to Wakan Tanka and, in the stillness, a wind springs from nowhere and rushes around the dance circle. We tremor as one.

At the end of the day, I return to the tree. I place my hand against its smooth bark and I pray. The sun dance chief takes the eagle feathers in my arms and pulls. My skin breaks and I am released.

At the feast that follows the dance, I am unready to return to this world. All about me people are celebrating. I hold a piece of watermelon in my mouth and marvel at the luxurious wetness of it. The sun dance chief invites me to come and dance next year on his family's land in South Dakota.

'Bring your son,' he says.

—

I say goodbye to all the people who have been part of this time. I farewell all the places too. California, Arizona, Utah, Colorado, Nevada, Oregon. Hours into the long flight to Australia across the Pacific Ocean, I am woken by a flight attendant. There are engine problems, she explains. The plane is being diverted to Honolulu.

We disembark. I am taken to a five-star hotel with a small group of passengers. I am told that all expenses will be paid by the airline. My room is large and overlooks a marina. I call Alastair and explain the delay. I can't sleep again so I fill the marble tub. I have only hand luggage with me and I'm dressed for the Melbourne winter that awaits me. After breakfast, I take a shuttle bus to a shopping centre and buy a pair of bathers. It is a perfect tropical day and I spend the morning at the beach swimming and reading. Back at the hotel, I eat lunch then nap. It feels decadent, this luxury, after the past few weeks.

Upon waking, I head to the rooftop pool for another swim. Some of my fellow passengers are there and recognise me. They invite me to join them for dinner. We eat a Japanese banquet, courtesy of the airline, and are bussed back to the airport for a midnight flight. My companions queue and it is only then I discover I've been mistaken for a first-class passenger. I am only travelling economy. When I find the right queue and check in, I learn that economy passengers have spent the last twenty-four hours in the airport. I settle into my seat at the back of the plane, amused and grateful for this unexpected gift. Spirit has an excellent sense of humour.

——

I return to Australia a pipe carrier. In Lakota lore, the original pipe was a gift from White Buffalo Calf Woman. She appeared first as a white buffalo, then transformed into a woman some 2000 years ago. She gave the people the seven sacred ceremonies. All pipes are connected back to that first pipe, which is kept by a Lakota family on Green Grass Reservation. Walking the red road of Lakota lore means to live a life governed by honesty, humility, compassion, respect, generosity and wisdom. It will also entail living up to the commitment I have made. Come what may, I have to return to America every year for the next three years. I have to dance. I do not know what will be asked of me nor who I will become on this red road, but I know it's too late to go back. I am going to have to find a way to live between two worlds.

TREE

Two roads diverged in a wood, and I –
I took the one less traveled by,
And that has made all the difference.

ROBERT FROST

When I arrive home from the sun dance, there is a chasm between me and Alastair. He doesn't ask for stories and he doesn't touch the holes in my arms. While those will heal, the rift between us will not.

Alastair and I begin the life of separated parents, transferring our little boy between us. It is incredibly hard. It is incredibly painful. We have been together since I was seventeen, renewing our relationship after the two years I was overseas. He has been a huge part of all that has shaped me as I grew to adulthood.

I move to a duplex with nothing but a rug and my writing desk, hoping that avoiding any financial acrimony will ensure an easier future between us. It does not. He will hardly speak to me again and, despite his increasing wealth, he will contribute the bare minimum to the raising of his only child.

I borrow a futon. I buy Christopher a bed and hang mobiles in his room. I stand in the whitegoods section of a store and consider my life ahead. I want there to be more family in the future but that seems unlikely. Choosing optimism, however, I buy a large fridge.

———

Somehow, I return to America each year. By now I have been lured back into an advertising agency where I am part of a team working on one of the largest accounts in Australia. I create branding and fashion advertising. Each winter, as part of the contract I negotiated, I take two months leave, pack my sun dance dresses and my medicine case, and return to ceremony. For the second dance and the fourth dance, Christopher comes with me. He is three years old and then he is five. We drive through farmlands and forests, over mountain passes, across deserts and prairies, and high up onto mesas of sagebrush and piñon trees, prickly pear and juniper. The car is full of Lego under construction. We sing and listen to audio books. When it isn't one of his audio books, it's Chris Isaak singing 'Blue Hotel'. That album seems to suit the landscape. Also Ry Cooder, the Eagles, Lyle Lovett, James Taylor, Neil Young, Ennio Morricone, Ella Fitzgerald, Etta James . . . We stop at the all-you-can-eat-for-two-dollars buffets in Nevada casinos. We discover biscuits and gravy and every kind of pie. Christopher eats around 100 hot dogs and another 100 pancakes. I drink litres of iced tea and fall in love with breakfast burritos.

Christopher learns to eat whatever he is fed on reservations and beyond: fry bread and mince, beef stew, corn, squash, chilli, beans, huevos rancheros and fried chicken. My rule is when we are on the road, we eat what we get and we don't complain. He grows very familiar with airports, with packing and unpacking, setting up camp and making friends.

We camp in state parks and national parks, in awe of the beauty of the American landscape. We stay on reservations and with fellow dancers and supporters. Sometimes we have a night at a cheap motel so we can take a bath and do the washing.

I can still see Chris at the edge of the sage circle, wearing his favourite red tracksuit even in that heat. I can see him running through the campground and sitting in the camp kitchen telling stories. I can see us lying under trees on green riverbanks, scrambling down into arroyos to swim, lying under the stars at 2000 metres, reading and talking by candle lantern in our tent.

He learns to swim in a pool in the mountains of Colorado. He also plays in snow for the first time in the Rockies. We scramble across the shell-encrusted hills in the Badlands of South Dakota. We watch an enormous bull buffalo cross our campsite near Wounded Knee. I'd never read *Bury My Heart at Wounded Knee*, about the displacement of Native Americans in the American West, but when I get out of the car and stand on the land, I am overwhelmed with sadness. Years later, when I visit the battlefield of Culloden in the Scottish Highlands, I'll have that same feeling. Land carries scars through time. Bodies carry memories through generations.

—

After my second dance on the reservation in South Dakota, as soon as I step outside the sage circle I am blinded. The world is too bright. Everything is irradiated by light. I worry I have done permanent damage, but more experienced dancers assure me it is all part of the dance. They care for me and they care for Christopher. On the fourth morning, I wake and I am able to see again.

With my sight restored, Christopher and I explore the Black Hills. We swim in lakes. We go to gatherings and other ceremonies. We see incredible thunderstorms with lightning that vivifies the night sky for minutes at a time. This four-year commitment brings extraordinary wonders.

—

But I am living two lives. One as a pipe carrier and a sun dancer, the other as a twenty-something woman, an advertising copy-writer, a single mum and the owner of a gorgeous '65 Mustang. My days are spent with production people, doing film shoots, radio commercials, pitches and presentations, making campaigns to sell the latest look, the latest season. Meanwhile, I am saving hard to get back to America year after year. Those two worlds could not be farther apart.

I dream of buying land up in the mountains of New Mexico and living there. It's remote, the sky a very particular blue, the people warm and creative. The clouds are almost as exuberant as they are in Tasmania. But I can't take Christopher away from his dad. I want to honour their father/son relationship. So, I stay on in Melbourne. I have no history here. In winter the concrete chills everything and the sky is low and grey, day after day. The summers are intensely hot without the reprieve of a sea breeze, and to drive to an ocean beach takes hours. I don't like the traffic or the relentless pace of life.

But Melbourne has a secret. It has spectacular sunsets. While peak hour sees the city gridlocked, a fiesta of colour goes on over Port Phillip Bay – gold, apricot, mauve and red. Christopher and I often walk the pier or climb a hill on the waterfront to watch the sun go down. We spend time with friends in the Daylesford area on weekends. It isn't the sea or rainforest, but it is breathing space away from the city. When Christopher is older, I tell myself, we'll live somewhere beautiful.

———

The fourth dance is held in New Mexico, south of Albuquerque, on private land. It is a small dance. Together with my fellow sun dancers, we clear a dance ground, we sweat in lodges and we look for a tree. This part of the desert is low and scrubby. Cottonwoods are hard to find. We plan an expedition further afield.

Christopher is creating a Lego spaceship in our tent. He is five now. He wants to stay in the tent, not come trawling across the countryside in search of a tree. For Indigenous Americans, all children are your children. Traditionally, any child that comes into your care, or your home, is treated with the love you would give your own children. So, I let everyone know where he is, and go off with my fellow dancers in search of a tree.

We traverse the desert in a four-wheel drive. It is 35 degrees with a hot wind and high white billowing clouds. Then a storm rolls in, moving fast as they do in this part of the world, darkening the horizon, obliterating the sun and consuming the light. Within minutes hail is drumming on the roof of the truck and battering the windows. Thunder, ear-splitting in strength, rolls above us. In seconds, the hot red sand of the road becomes mud and we are mired here.

Daniel, a sun dance brother, strips off his shirt and jumps out of the car, laughing and leaping about in the rain. Water is filling every furrow, dip and hollow. Then the lightning comes, great sheets of it. The air is electric, raising the hair on my arms, the hair on my head. We watch, stranded and sublimated by the cacophony overhead, marooned by water. We are in search of a ceremonial tree and the thunder beings have come to play. In Lakota lore, the thunder beings are buffalo stampeding across the sky. We must wait until they pass, and they take their time.

Someone suggests that maybe our sun dance chief has arrived at camp. We laugh. Of course.

The sun dance chief who leads us in my third and fourth years is also Lakota, from a lineage of sun dancers and sun dance chiefs. His chest and back are woven with scars from years of ceremony. He is a good man, funny, full of stories. And he is like the truck driver in Douglas Adams' *Hitchhiker's Guide to the Galaxy*. Everywhere he goes, he brings the rain. Last year I gave him an Australian Driza-Bone raincoat. He loved it, but a few days later I saw him give it away to a relative who admired it, because that's the traditional way. Possessions are held lightly. Nature, life and the spirits are the real gifts. You have to be careful when admiring a rug or a blanket in the home of Lakota, because they'll try to give it to you. That's the meaning of the misused term *Indian giving*. It is complete trust in the flow of life, true and unattached generosity.

Sure enough, when we arrive back at camp some three hours later, our sun dance chief has arrived. He'd had car trouble out in South Dakota which delayed him for several days. While everyone else was chatting about the storm, I was desperate to find Christopher. He was in the camp kitchen with friends. He told me the storm was so loud he'd climbed into his sleeping bag and fallen asleep. He'd woken only a few minutes before I arrived back.

Still, we have no tree. We need a cottonwood that is not too big, a forked tree to take the dancers' ropes, a tree accessible enough to put on a flat-bed truck and bring it back to the dance ground, a tree not too big to lower with ropes and pulleys onto the truck. We pray, but two more days pass and there is still no tree. We make flesh offerings and wrap them in prayer ties. We give the skin of our bodies and we pray some more.

The following day, a landowner a few miles away, hearing of our plight, suggests we look on his property. We take a tree from his land in a dawn ceremony, wrapping every branch within a blanket of tarpaulins, taking every twig and leaf, transporting it all to camp then carrying it into the dance ground.

This is my commitment. For my first year, I danced with one feather in each arm for a single day. For my second dance, two feathers in each arm for two days. Third dance, three feathers, three days. Now it is my fourth dance. The feathers I use are Australian wedge-tailed eagle feathers, gifted to me by a senior Aboriginal man who has become a friend.

In the first round of the first day, I go to the tree and the sun dance chief pierces each of my arms four times, then he ties a feather into each wound. Being pierced early puts me inside the dance fast. Immediately I am in that other world, floating through the grey dawns with frost burning my feet and through the afternoons when the baking earth scalds them. Through songs and sweat lodges. I love being inside these ways again. We are a small, close community of dancers and supporters. Some of us have danced all four years together.

On the last round of the last day, I go to the tree. A sun dance brother stands on either side of me. In unison, they tear the feathers, one by one, from my arms. I feel myself shoot up the tree. I do not stop. I continue up into the sky and right out into the stars. I drift there in the beyond and it is peaceful. I am in that other place where we are infinite, in the void that seems to contain nothing and everything. Then the dance calls me back. The drum, the song. Christopher calls me back. Life calls me back.

As I drop from the sky, back down the tree and into my body, I feel the tree let me go. I feel the dance let me go. I feel the commitment I made four years ago let me go. It is as if something or someone has shut a door in front of me. Something I have been listening to for four years has stopped. The silence is unnerving.

Around me, the dance is concluding. The last songs are being sung. The last men are breaking from the tree. I'd made a commitment to dance for four years and I had kept my promise despite all sorts of obstacles. But I'd imagined I would always come back. Whether as a helper, cooking, supporting or dancing, I didn't know, but I had planned on returning year after year. I never thought I'd leave these ways, nor that they would leave me. What did it mean for it to come to an end, to feel complete? I was free but did I want that? Who was I beyond dancing?

I camp with fellow sun dancers for the four days of integration after the dance. We find a lake and swim. It has been sixteen days since Christopher and I have washed or bathed. In photos taken then I am wafer-thin, my eyes huge in my face after four days of fasting. But it is more than that. It is a thinness after four years of dancing, four years of paying acute attention to everything this commitment has asked of me. Four years of participating in a ceremony that has been with me every day of the year, honing a sense in me for the unseen, the surreal, the subtle and the intrinsic. Nothing was as it had been before I started to dance. Nothing was as it had been before I entered that first sweat lodge ceremony and saw two red eyes.

I was a sun dancer. What did that mean in the twentieth century? The word *sacred* means *to be regarded with reverence*. Some people believe churches are sacred. Temples, mosques, monasteries, stupas, synagogues, walls, too. Religious books – the Quran, the Bible, the Vedic scriptures, the Buddhist scriptures, scrolls, poems, shastra, stotras and sutras. Gods and goddesses, prophets and teachers, saints and walis, mountains, rocks and buttes, rivers and lacunas have all been declared sacred. Some people feel that way about fishing and even football. I regarded nature with reverence. Oceans, beaches, mountains, wild rivers, old trees, lakes and forests. Through sun dancing, I lost my sense of a limited world. Everything was permeable, malleable, responsive. I was in relationship with everything here – animate and inanimate, large and small, creature, human, other. I was related . . . *mitakuye oyasin.*

—

We return to Australia. I go back to work. Christopher and his dad resume their schedule, spending every second weekend together. The wounds on my arms heal. I gain some weight. I've been on the road in my heart and my head for a long time. The tree has let me go and I have to move on. Every day I wonder when life will feel normal again.

I'm no longer required to live as a dancer, perform daily rituals, keep my focus on another year when I'll return to America and resume that other life. I want to be ordinary. I want to be like a regular thirty-year-old.

Intent on gluing the fragile parts of myself back together again, I put away my sun dance dresses. I wrap my feathers and pipe, stowing them in my medicine case with my fan, herbs, beads, felt and leather. I put the case on top of the wardrobe and I try to forget. But ravens have a way of turning up. Signs that I am connected, still connected, to the earth, to the spirit world, keep coming.

I thought, and hoped, normality would return after a few weeks passed, but it didn't. I could feel the pain and suffering in people I passed on the street. I could see it in their faces and in their eyes. I felt like a windvane attuned to a weather system of energy. Things came at me – pictures, visions and notions – and I didn't know how to deflect them or what to do with them. Being out in public became overwhelming. It was painful to be so open.

Then a man I'd met at sun dance, the only other Australian I'd ever met on the journey, invited me to the Central Desert of Australia for an Aboriginal dance. He suggested that Uluru would ground me. I wanted him to be right.

RAINBOW

The only sin is the sin of seriousness.

OSHO

I invite my boyfriend – let's call him Adam – to come with me to the Central Desert. We've been together almost a year. By day he is a freelance art director in advertising and by night a singer/songwriter waiting for his big break. He's talented. His band plays regular gigs in Melbourne and Sydney and gets good airplay on the radio. Adam can be romantic, funny, generous and thoughtful. His dad died suddenly when he was seven. My brother died suddenly when I was twelve. We are united in our sense that death can come at any moment. Living is important.

He was brought up a devout Baptist and is the black sheep of his family because he smokes and drinks and hasn't been to church in years. His three sisters are all married to Baptist ministers. Maybe it's an act of rebellion to date me, a single mother who's never been married. He doesn't want to know about sun dancing or Indigenous ways. To him I am a girl with a cool car, a certain look and an excellent stereo system.

I have a career in advertising and I want to write novels. That's enough. Anything that hints at religion repels him.

Adam isn't sure about coming to the desert. He runs hot and cold. There are proclamations of love – accompanied by romantic notes, song lyrics and gifts – but then he wavers.

I say, 'Look, if it doesn't go well, we'll break up after the trip. But it would be fun to go camping in the desert together.'

So, he agrees.

—

The scars are still fresh on my arms, my body thin, my mind still raw and vulnerable when I arrive in the desert. Indigenous Tasmanians have a history flowing back more than 60,000 years. Their culture was decimated, their land, languages and ceremonies largely lost. In the Central Desert, though, there are still ceremonies that have been performed for millennia. I am keen to participate if I am permitted.

But when we arrive in Alice Springs, we are informed that the dance we'd been invited to has been cancelled. Instead, arrangements are made for us to camp on an old homestead some hours out of Alice.

Two of the leaders of the trip have a spiritual centre in the foothills of Melbourne. Before the centre, they were senior professionals in academia and health. They've been exploring the depths of the human mind, body and soul for more than thirty years, leading workshops, teaching healing modalities, building community. Let's call them Mars and Venus.

Sun dancing is by no means the harshest of ceremonies, but it's tough. In comparison, I found a lot of New Age stuff flimsy. If there wasn't pain and suffering, I wasn't sure it was valid. Now, finding myself led by Mars and Venus rather than Indigenous people, I'm uncomfortable. I'm not sure I'm in the right place.

—

I've never been to the Central Desert before and the country is breathtaking – rich pink and orange sand, a cloudless turquoise sky. The nightscape is vivid with more stars, planets and constellations than I have ever seen. We set up camp along a dry river bed.

In Central Australia the heat ripples. It stretches. It leans into me and weighs down my limbs. It insists that I slow. Pause. Be. I hadn't understood the concept of the *Dreamtime* until I found myself in a 48-degree day. To survive, some part of me has to leave my body. I sit with my back against a gum tree and drop into meditation. I glimpse how creation stories have been summoned through the heat and the stars.

Mars and Venus invite us to find a spirit name to guide us through our time here. It's a bit weird, this process, but I sit out on a hill in the desert amid grasses and insects. It is two months after sun dance and I feel as transient as a breeze. The name that comes to me is 'One with the Wind'. A few days later, that name becomes a camp joke. But by then, I don't know what a joke is, nor can I tell you my name.

—

The men go off with Mars for a night and we women stay behind with Venus. We meditate deep into the night, the air warm and soft. I feel as if I am a traveller in the amphitheatre of the universe. My plan to become more grounded isn't working.

When the men return late in the morning, we share a midday feast in a shaded area. Then someone looks up and points to a rainbow that has formed in a perfect circle around the sun. The sky is cloudless, the rainbow startlingly bright. Then another rainbow appears, a larger circle around the smaller one. We stare at these two radiant rings of colour. Let me be clear: there are no drugs involved in any of this. No alcohol. We are wide awake and sober.

Mars and Venus call us together, inviting us to make two circles, mirroring the rainbows above: an inner circle and an outer circle. We join hands and our circles start revolving, one clockwise, the other anticlockwise. We lift our faces to the sky. We begin to sing an ancient Hindu mantra – 'Om Namah Shivaya'. It's a Hindu blessing of earth, fire, water, air and ether. After years of sun dancing, looking into the sun doesn't worry me, so I also stare into the sun.

Something powerful begins to move as we circle in our impromptu rainbow dance. A rippling of energy like a spirit wind at sun dance. We all feel it. We keep holding hands, circling and singing, staring up at the double rainbow.

I see a figure emerge within the vivid orb of the sun and walk towards me. It is crossing dimensions, a silhouette against the light, but a human form, coming fast. I don't question it. I don't resist. I've seen stranger things at sun dance. I could no more have stopped it than halted an ocean wave. When it reaches me, a blast of electricity fells me. I drop into nothingness.

—

What I don't know until much later is that other people drop too, collapsing, blacking out. Their descriptions of this force that hits them vary. Whatever it is, Mars and Venus and other teachers on this trip try to contain it, but it is immense. Of the forty-two people there, twelve of us lose our faculties for hours, six of us lose our faculties for days and months. One of us ends up in the psychiatric unit of the Alice Springs hospital. Some of us go mad years later. One of us dies early, in a sudden brain event. Everyone who was there remembers the time with hushed awe. And we laugh, too, because there is no ordinary explanation.

—

Meanwhile, I have lost all sense of *I*. There is no self. No sense of the singular. Whatever is now, is aware. It observes. It is *being*. *Being* is light on every surface, and the play of shadow, too. The texture of darkness and the colours of the world. The fluidity of water, the curiousness of sound, the murmur of grasses, the eddies of air, the density of rock and its porousness. *Being* observes things that are light and can fly and things that are weighty and only walk. *Being* observes structures to shelter and shade, implements and vessels for purpose. *Being* observes other beings who walk and hold and sit. *Being* is consciousness. The being that is me, the vessel that holds me, the experiences beyond my skin and inside my skin, it is all part of one creation.

Venus ensures my being is undisturbed. She is often near me, sitting at the opening to the tent. (I could not have spoken its name back then. It is observed as the thing that softens the light. Nothing has a name.) *Being* has no needs or desires. *Being* has no time or words. *Being* is calm, fulfilled and effortless.

—

Mars and Venus call it 'an expansion'. A spiritual expansion – an opportunity for cosmic consciousness to occupy us brought on by the electrifying force in the circle. We are dwelling in an altered and expanded perception of reality. Mars and Venus ensure we have quiet and rest to reconstitute our identities. 'Coming back in,' they call it.

One of us, Stella, goes quite mad. Venus takes her to Alice Springs, where she is hospitalised. The psychiatrist diagnoses a psychotic break and plans to commit her, but Venus is not sure a psychiatric unit is the right place for Stella. In her Melbourne life, Stella is an actress. At a critical moment in her psychiatric assessment, Venus whispers to her, 'Act sane.' The highly trained Stella does, and together they walk out of the hospital and are transported back into the tender care of the group. It will be several years before Stella feels normal again. Her whole life beyond the desert is upended. It is a story of love, death and celebration, but it's Stella's to tell, not mine.

I, too, am having a break but mine is delightful, enervating and blissful. I am in love with everything and everyone. I am without vocabulary, identity, geography, history. I am dislocated from self and memories. In my stillness, there is only the moment. And the next moment. The hills are luminous, plants are luminous, people are luminous. Everything is movement and vibration. Nothing is solid. It all moves. It is all sound. Light is filled with sound. Sunrise has a sound. Night has a sound. Stars have a long, low sound. I am in the immensity of existence. The sun passes, the night sky, too, heat and breeze flow over me, around me and through me. There is no future or past. Only the wondrous now.

This goes on until one day I notice a tiny thing flickering in the great expanse I inhabit. The flickering thing is in a distant region far away. At first, it is no bigger than a thumbnail in a concert hall, but it twinkles and catches my attention. Eventually my awareness swoops down to take a closer look.

The flickering thing has images on it. When I look more closely, the images grow bigger. I am trying to grasp language again, to speak with the humans around me. A series of shapes appear on the screen. I sound out the shapes. People seem pleased I have spoken. It is helpful, this screen.

The more time I spend with the screen, the more it grows. I tell Venus about it. She explains that I am seeing things from the past. Facts, recollections, memories of Heather. I begin to comprehend that a human life *is* the screen. Mostly, we have no idea it is a screen. We call it reality.

I am both a being called Heather and something else beyond the screen, a vastness of energy and flow. I can use the screen to gather information for the human experience. In *Star Trek* there is a virtual world called the holodeck where the crew can play with different roles and environments. The screen is the holodeck for a human life. I am captivated, enchanted, fascinated by everything on the screen, even when I know it isn't real. I have been in some kind of universal mind, without a screen, but slowly my individual mind is returning.

—

Later, people will tell me stories of this time. Once I started talking again, I referred to people as their identities. Mars was 'the Mars', Venus 'the Venus'. I would say, 'It is not a hurry thing,' to suggest people could slow down – immediately or in general.

Someone renames me. I am not One with the Wind; I am Gone with the Wind.

One day, Venus and I are wandering close to camp. I lean down to observe the passage of ants across the surface of a rock. I say, 'There is a child. These' – I indicate the ants – 'say there is a child.'

It dawns on her. 'Yes, sweetheart, you have a child back in Melbourne. His name is Christopher. You love him very much.'

The Heather-entity has a child. This is new information. I discover that the screen gives me access to everything Heather has stored away. *Data. Files. Memories.* Information about my individual self.

—

Adam asks me to marry him out in the desert. He, too, was knocked down by the inexplicable force, but he quickly recovered. He was distressed by my situation but Venus reassured him I simply needed time to be.

I'm not sure what he means when he proposes, but love is evident. Love and caring. The Heather-being likes love and caring. Venus tells us this is no time to be making decisions.

One morning, the group goes off to participate in a ceremony in the foothills. Adam stays behind to look after me. We make love for the first time since the double rainbow.

Some days later, we are on the bus heading back to Alice Springs. I look out the window and see something flying across the desert, covering a huge distance at speed. It is a butterfly. It flies through the glass of the bus window and enters my ear. It says, 'You are going to have a baby.'

I turn to Adam and say, 'There is going to be a baby.'

—

To return to Melbourne, we must fly. It is an ordinary Qantas domestic flight. I am disoriented and disturbed as we enter the plane. It's as if I am trying to squeeze myself into a sardine tin. This weird machine to move me from one location to another is too small. It's the first time I experience pain and distress. Apparently, I make quite a spectacle of myself. Venus sits beside me and soothes me until I fall asleep.

—

The world beyond the desert, I discover, is complex. *Being* isn't how the world is designed. Humans are about *Doing*. Venus wants me to come and stay at their centre up in the hills. She says things like this happen so rarely in a human life, and I should immerse myself in the experience. But I know the Heather-being went to the desert to try to find normality. And I have a son who needs me. Adam, too, wants me to come home. We don't live together, but there is a wedding to plan and a future. He needs me to be normal, to be my old self. I want that too.

I sense that words are important to the Heather-being, as I still think of myself. But vast tracts of my brain are inaccessible or obliterated. My vocabulary is haphazard. When the brain cannot recall a word, the screen makes syllables appear and I repeat them. It's the same with information about practical matters. I cannot go back to work so I take leave. I access the Heather memories to drive a car, do the shopping, keep house, make phone calls. Slowly things start to coalesce.

Christopher goes at just the right speed for me. He likes the same outdoor life. He finds the same things funny. We spend a lot of time lying about in the local park observing the grass and insects, clouds and ducks. He reads his picture books to me. He points out words and sounds things out for me. I learn to read again, or remember how to read. I make my way from picture books to children's novels, until I am reading adult novels again. All this reading, the ordinary life of mothering, being in the world, it helps my mind begin to fill in the gaps. I lose the distance between myself and the screen. I integrate the old with the new.

Eventually I go back to work. Everyone in the creative department of an advertising agency is eccentric, so I fit in just fine.

—

Has my mind ever been the same since the desert? No. Those of us who were most affected by whatever happened under that double rainbow, we steadied, healed, reintegrated, surrendered to the strangeness of it all and went on. But not all of us. The ripples continued for a long time.

—

Vocabulary was the hardest thing to relearn after the desert. It was difficult to recall the most obvious words. I remember trying to find the word for the vessel that carried things around. The screen in my mind typed the word 'backpack' on it. How hilarious this arrangement of letters was as I sounded them out. *Backpack.*

All objects were curious and wondrous for a long time. There was delight in discovering everything and everyone. A saucepan. A shoe. Two shoes. Two socks. A pillow. A friend. It still happens from time to time. I lose vocabulary when I'm tired or unwell. Recently, I was trying to explain to my second son, the one conceived in the desert, that I wanted something to happen. I grappled for the word but ended up saying 'sometime a short way ahead but not too distant'. 'Soon, Mumma?' he suggested, and we laughed.

—

Adam and I are married on a 37-degree day at a lavender farm outside Melbourne. I am eighteen weeks pregnant. We move to Tasmania a few months later. He imagines a sea change: we will live in a rambling house, me writing novels, him making music. We almost buy a cottage on fifteen acres of land, but instead settle on a house in the centre of Hobart, five minutes from an advertising agency that offers us work and seven minutes from good coffee for Adam.

The first night back in Tasmania, staying near the River
Derwent, I hear a sentence come in on the evening breeze.
My brother Ambrose is a tiger hunter. It is the first sentence of
a novel I will write over the coming three years, the first to
be published. Adam starts an advertising business. I write the
words and he art-directs. When we win a federal government
contract, he continues as creative director and I become the
managing director. Soon there are staff and clients to care for,
work to create and produce, balance sheets, budgets, taxes and
contracts. Running a business is a steep learning curve, but
I read a lot of books, get a good mentor and take some courses.
The mortgage, the school fees, the food on the table, it all relies
on the agency being a success.

I am a mum, a wife, a friend, a daughter, a business owner
and employer. Life is too busy for meditation. There is hardly
a moment to be still. But I learn to find the sacred within the
overflow of life. In the brief silence of a car trip. On camping
trips with the children. On the morning walks I take in the
foothills of the mountain behind our home. On starry nights
on the balcony watching city and sky. Lighting candles for the
dinner table. Wrapping the body of a beloved pet in red cloth,
sprinkling it with sage and tobacco, before the children and I lay
it to rest in the earth. Even in the hardest times, when finding
love seems impossible – love of myself, love of my body with its
unpredictable health, love of my marriage – there are always
birds and clouds, a child bringing laughter, a friend bringing
delight, a feeling of being connected to something bigger, even
if that thread feels like a filament of gossamer.

I'm committed to being human. I'm in love with this planet and the people who inhabit it. We are all learning. It feels like an achievement in itself, being alive. I'm grateful for it all. I'm grateful every day. Living this human life with love is a full-time occupation.

Whatever happened under the double rainbow in the desert was ultimately beyond words. Watching movies of cosmic encounters, I feel comforted. Seeing the angels on the beach at sunrise in *City of Angels*, I am moved to tears.

—

But before all this, back in Melbourne, I am pregnant. Christopher had been a straightforward labour, so I imagine this baby will have the same. It is not to be. At thirty-five weeks the placenta shears away from the wall of my womb, cutting off blood flow and oxygen to the baby. It's called a placental abruption, and usually both mother and baby die. Luckily, I know none of this as I am transported to Monash Hospital by ambulance after haemorrhaging in the bath at home.

Doctors swirl about me, urging me to sign a form for a caesarean. My home birth midwife arrives at the hospital. 'I don't want a caesarean,' I say to her, as armfuls of blood-soaked sheets are carried past by the ambulance officers who transported me here. I faint. I've been doing this since getting out of the bath. My blood pressure is sixty over forty and dropping. The midwife pushes a clipboard and pen into my hand and says, 'Sign the form or your baby will die.'

I sign. And faint again. I come around to find nurses running me on a gurney down a corridor and into an operating theatre.

An anaesthetist puts a line in my arm. 'What's your blood type?' he barks at me.

'B positive,' I say. I don't like him being grumpy at a moment like this, so I add, 'That's my rule for life as well.'

The harassed expression evaporates and he laughs. Then I am gone into anaesthesia.

—

When I resurface, Adam passes a little person to me. He says, 'Here's our baby Byron.'

Throughout the pregnancy, I was sure I was having a girl. We were going to name her Jessie after Nan Rose. We only mentioned a boy's name once. I'd said, 'If it's a boy, and I'm pretty sure it won't be, do you think we could call him Byron?' Adam agreed. It was the only conversation we had about it.

If I'd been awake, if the birth had been normal, I don't think I could have gone ahead with calling him Byron. It was too painful. But I'd lost more than a third of my blood, and my brain wasn't working properly.

For days I couldn't tell if this baby was my brother Byron or a new Byron, my son. I couldn't tell if I was a mother or a sister. I couldn't stop weeping and I didn't know if I was happy or sad. Had my brother come back, or had he never died? Maybe this baby was him again, or maybe it wasn't. I whispered, *Byron . . . Byron*, and I didn't know if it was the right thing or a terrible thing to have summoned this name back into our family. But everyone was calling him Byron. It was too late to change it.

Because he had been in such a hurry to save Byron, the surgeon had made a long jagged cut across my belly. It was hard to walk, hard to move. Blood loss made me faint if I stood up or moved about. I refused a transfusion, thinking I would be fine, but it would be months before I could climb the stairs in our house. Months before exhaustion finally departed. If I had my time over, I'd take the transfusion.

Meanwhile Byron smiled. He smiled all the time. When he was awake, when he fed, when he slept. Adam took a photo of him at just an hour old and he was already smiling.

Born five weeks early, he was covered in vernix, the thick creamy ointment that coats the skin of babies in the womb. He had no eyelashes or fingernails. No toenails either. He weighed just five pounds. Even 0000 clothes were big on him. But despite having been born in such dramatic circumstances, he was fine. In fact, he seemed enormously happy to be alive.

Girlfriends brought lamps, pillows and blankets to our hospital room and turned off the fluorescent lights. On the door they hung a sign: *Sacred space. Newborn and mother within. Please use a gentle voice.* They brought me soups and smoothies. I woke and slept and Byron did the same. He was tucked in with me, skin to skin, breastfeeding as he needed to, reproducing as best we could the weeks of the pregnancy when he would still have been inside the world of my womb.

'He's a little miracle,' the surgeon said. 'There was blood and meconium in the amniotic fluid. He almost drowned.'

———

My brother Byron drowned. My baby Byron nearly drowned in my womb, but he didn't. We both survived.

PORTAL

. . . she wanted to step off the world and slip away
into starlight. She was sure that was the way home.

THE MUSEUM OF MODERN LOVE

When Byron is five and Christopher eleven years old, I get a call from my sister who is living in Queensland. She tells me Nan Burgess is in hospital in Hobart. She's had a stroke and is not going to recover. We'd been living in Tasmania for six years by then, but Mum hadn't called me to let me know.

I go to the hospital and find Nan in a private room. She is dying, unable to wake or speak, but I can see from her face that she is in pain. Nan has had arthritis for many years – rheumatoid arthritis and osteoporosis. The knuckles on her fine hands, all her joints, are severely inflamed. I know what arthritis pain feels like. I can't understand why she is not being given medication.

My sister is a highly trained emergency nurse. She flies to Hobart, and we go into the hospital together. She takes one look at Nan then speaks with the staff, nurse to nurse, and organises a syringe driver. Almost instantly, Nan's beautiful face softens into the face we have loved all our lives. We bathe her hands and feet, brush her shining white hair and wet her mouth with a special sponge. We chat to her about things we remember from our childhood. From time to time she moves a little or murmurs, as if to assure us that she knows we are there.

We thank her for all the afternoon teas, the walks on the rocks at Howden, the swims in North West Bay, the swims at White Beach. For all the times at the shack, and the funny frosty ways she had of showing that she loved us. We share stories of her and Grandad and their little blue Volkswagen with its camper trailer on the back. We tell her how she'd taught us to be fiercely independent and use our intelligence.

I remind her that when I moved into rental accommodation, she gave me a double bed mattress. I went to pick it up with Alastair and, as we left with it roped to the top of the station wagon, she'd called out mischievously, 'Have fun!'

She'd shown us what the love of a good man looked like. Grandad had been her champion, her hero, her friend and her great love. She'd watched him drown as she stood on the shore at Lime Bay. She'd watched her grandson drown with him.

—

The next morning, I wake at 6 am. I have an intense feeling that I need to get down to the hospital. We have a new member of the family, another miracle of conception and my last baby. Elliotte is blonde-haired and blue-eyed. When I first look into her eyes, she feels like an old friend returned. Our family is complete.

By 7 am Elliotte and I are at Nan's bedside and her breathing is erratic. I ask the staff to call my sister and our mum. At first Elliotte is happy on my lap, but then she becomes restless and I put her on the floor where she practises her new art of sitting up.

I hold Nan's hand. I begin singing 'Om Namah Shivaya', the same song we'd sung in the desert under the double rainbow. My strictly atheist Nan, convinced that dying meant going into the ground to become worm food, was having a sacred Hindu song sung to her in the last hours of her life, but I didn't think she'd mind.

The intervals between Nan's breaths grow longer and longer. Sometimes it feels like minutes between one breath and the next. Then something extraordinary happens. I can see the palest veils of lemon, pink, mauve, blue and silver floating up and away from her, disappearing into the air above her. Is it her aura departing?

Then a presence arrives in the room. It is invisible but palpable. I feel certain someone is standing above Nan's bed, as if they had opened a door in the wall. In London, I'd been with a beloved employer in his final hours of life, but there'd been nothing like this, although I hadn't been in the room when he died. Nan doesn't believe in an afterlife. She doesn't believe in spirits or the supernatural. She is endlessly practical and pragmatic.

Then I think of Elliotte. Why is my six-month-old baby so quiet on the floor? I turn and see that she is staring up at the wall behind Nan's bed – at the place where I'm sure there is a presence. She's transfixed, eyes wide and shining, mouth open, as if she is seeing someone, or something, familiar. Whatever it is, it gives me goosebumps.

I return my attention to Nan and continue singing. A little while later, Nan inhales and then quietly exhales. I wait, but she does not breathe again. I have the distinct sense she has walked away with the person behind the bed.

Time stills. The room is hushed. The portal between this world and beyond seems to have closed. I continue holding Nan's hand. Elliotte sits on the floor, also silent. We are lost in reverie.

Then time returns. My sister comes through the door. She hugs me and says very gently, 'Hello, sweet. You can let go now.'

I look at Nan. She has the waxen face of a dead person. It startles me. Her body is quite empty of her; nothing of the Nan I've known remains. I slip my hand from hers and kiss her one last time. Only then does Elliotte start to fuss.

After Nan's death, I think about who might accompany me in the last hour of my life. A grandchild I am yet to meet? A great-grandchild? It gives me a new regard for family.

Since that morning, I have never doubted that when we die, regardless of what we believe, someone familiar comes to guide us into whatever is beyond this life. We do not do this alone.

MOUNTAIN

*Life is no 'brief candle' for me. It is a sort of splendid
torch which I have got hold of for the moment,
and I want to make it burn as brightly as possible
before handing it on to future generations.*

GEORGE BERNARD SHAW

When Christopher is almost fourteen, I suggest we walk seventy kilometres through the heart of Tasmania's Central Highlands on the Overland Track. To my surprise, he agrees.

It's been a crazy year. My children are very different ages. Chris, being the eldest, is often at the end of the line for attention and parenting. It feels like the whole year has gone by and I've had ten minutes with him. I've yearned for time alone together, with no siblings, emails, phone calls, meetings or distractions to get in the way.

Two nights before our departure, I pore over the map and guidebook and consider how foolhardy I've been. Of late, my survival skills have been reduced to a weekly game of hockey.

Are we really going to walk seventy kilometres in the wild together?

Since the arrival of pubic hair, Chris mostly converses in grunts and grimaces. I know that if I wait another year, he'll never agree to do this walk with me. It might be years before he and I will spend a whole week together alone again.

I have raised the idea of a father/son rite of passage with his father and his stepfather to farewell boyhood and welcome Chris to manhood, but neither father is keen. It feels important to acknowledge this time for Chris. A mother offering a son this moment of transition isn't ideal, but with the men not wanting to show up, I will have to suffice.

Chris is nearing six feet tall. Multiple loaves of bread and packets of cereal are devoured each week. I ponder how much he might eat when walking in the wilds with a pack on his back, so I cook and dehydrate day and night. Tasmania's weather is notoriously changeable and the highlands are prone to extremes. Even in summer, it might snow. It could rain every day. There will be mosquitoes, ants, snakes and teenage mood swings. There may be injuries, hypothermia, frostbite or sunburn. But as I listen to the hum of the food dryer whirring away in the kitchen, I know we will not starve.

Adam drives us north to the start of the walking track. Elliotte is now two years old, Byron seven. They read, eat and chatter in the car. Chris is subdued. He listens to music on his headphones and pretends we are not part of his world. The last two days he's been voicing his concerns. *I'd rather stay home than go on a walk. I'm on holiday – why are you dragging me off like this? I don't want to walk seventy kilometres.*

We get out of the car and put the last items into our packs. Chris says, 'I could be at home playing on the computer. I could be riding my bike. I could be doing anything but going on a walk you want me to do.'

'You'll remember this your whole life,' I say.

'Big deal,' he replies.

'You said you wanted to do it,' I remind him.

'I said maybe.'

We both know this is untrue.

'Well, it's a bit late to back out now,' I say, surveying the start of the track across the road.

'We don't have to go,' he says. 'We could just stay here.'

'Yeah, we could,' I agree, heaving the pack from the ground and wrangling it onto my back. 'But let's do it. It'll be great.'

'I think we're making a big mistake,' Chris says.

—

That first day is blue and hot. The view across the alpine moor is breathtaking. It is 3.30 pm when I sign us into the walkers registration book. The trek to our first overnight campsite is meant to take four hours. It's December, so it won't get dark until 9 pm. Still, it is later than I wanted to be leaving and I am keen to get underway.

I've waited twenty years to do this walk. When I was eighteen, I met a French couple who'd just arrived at the other end of the walk at Lake St Clair. They were so alive. I wanted to know that feeling of emerging from days of walking in the wild. It seemed ridiculous that so many years had passed between then and now. How does so much happen in a life?

In the national park there is no electricity, no hot showers and no mobile coverage. If something were to happen, it is up to us to perform first aid or effect a rescue. In emergencies, a rescue helicopter can land at the overnight camping spots, but you could wait a long time out here with a broken leg, a snakebite or a head injury. Such joyful thoughts accompany me as the afternoon heat intensifies. The pack settles into a tough weight on my shoulders and already my feet are feeling hot in my boots.

The first part of the walk is across a buttongrass plain. Our footsteps ring hollow on the duckboards. We reach stairs that rise up into forest. After the first long flight, Chris says, 'It's a mistake. I should never have agreed. Nothing good is going to come of this walk.'

I strap the hot spot on my heel and we slug water from our flasks. After two kilometres we are in rainforest. A river rushes over dark overhangs through a gully. Shafts of light catch on small alpine leaves. We sit on a bench by the side of the path and mosquitoes home in. Chris is not happy. His calf muscles hurt. He refuses a piece of apricot delight. Through the trees, we can glimpse the car park in the distance. I watch as our four-wheel drive pulls out onto the road and drives off. We are on our own. Together.

Before we left, a friend said to me, 'The first day will silence him, but then you'll be right.' It isn't true about the silence. Chris complains loudly all the way up to the lookout. 'You made me come. Why couldn't you have done it with someone else? I'm going to hate you by the end of this . . . If you want me to keep walking, you're going to have to pay me . . . What are

NOTHING BAD EVER HAPPENS HERE

we going to do all day? Boring. It's going to be boring . . . My legs are really hurting . . . My shoulders are hurting . . . This is too hard . . . My pack's too heavy . . . You'll have to carry it for me . . .'

And then he realises he's left his book in the car. *The Hitchhiker's Guide to the Galaxy Quartet.* It's a favourite and he's devastated. 'The only thing I was looking forward to was lying in the tent and reading, and now I can't even do that.'

The climb to the lookout is vertical. It's an unexpected start to the walk, and it certainly silences me. With full packs on our backs, we use the chains on the path to haul ourselves up the white granite. We reach the summit and, after he catches his breath, Chris says, 'You said it was going to be an easy walk. I'll never believe anything you say again . . .'

From the lookout we can see for miles in every direction. I eye a ridge of mountains to the south that looks familiar.

'That's where we're going,' I say.

'You've got to be joking,' he replies.

We resume walking.

By the time we reach a rustic emergency hut over the escarpment, we are only halfway to the first night's camping spot. Chris's eyes are filled with tears as he takes off his pack.

'I can't do it – I just can't,' he says, resting his head on my shoulder. Suddenly he is seven again. I am no longer the adult who gets in the way of screen time or hounds him about doing his chores. I am his mum. I stroke his head then feed him rye bread and cheese, chocolate and water. I could send him back and go on alone. It would be hard. I'd have to carry the tent, as well as other things he is carrying at this point. All the food has been weighed and measured for two. But if he gives up, if he walks back to where Adam and his siblings are staying overnight, what will he learn from that? If he doesn't conquer sore legs or the fear of not being strong enough, fit enough, capable enough, how will that affect him?

We've talked about this first day being the toughest and the longest. Eleven kilometres. After this it is easier. Everyone says so. In six days, this walk will be over. But here, with my fragile teenager, six days feels like six years.

The sun is moving towards the horizon. I have to trust that Chris can do this. Somehow, we'll get to Waterfall Valley by nightfall. The last thing Chris needs is to turn around, go home, and live with the story that he doesn't have what it takes. When he has eaten and rested, we go on.

My father always said on family walks, 'The slowest walker sets the pace.' Chris leads and I follow. Snow drifts lie across the path. Today it is 25 degrees without a cloud in sight, but yesterday it snowed. This is typical for these mountains, and for Tasmania. We refill our drink bottles from one of the many alpine springs dotted along the path. The water tastes of sky and stone. It is delicious.

At ten-minute intervals, Chris stops, takes off his pack and says, 'Why are we doing this? I hate you. I don't want to go any further. I want to go back.' Then he says, 'Do you think we could call the rescue helicopter and I could break my arm?'

The rugged wall of Cradle Mountain slowly recedes behind us.

'The first day is miserable – that's what they say, isn't it?' he asks at the next stop.

'Yes,' I reply.

'You know, I could be at home right now, lying on the couch watching television.'

'You wouldn't be seeing that if you were,' I say, indicating Barn Bluff silhouetted against a tangerine sky.

'No, that's true,' he replies. 'So, we're going to eat the heaviest dinner tonight, right?'

'Sure,' I agree.

'Why do people your age have to come out to places like this?' he asks. 'You know you've got all this technology, modern inventions, and you need to come out here and be utterly primitive.'

'Maybe because we really get a sense of ourselves out here,' I suggest.

'Who wants to get a sense of themselves?' he replies, but he is smiling. 'So, only three hours tomorrow? I'm going to sleep in until ten.'

'Shh,' he adds. 'I think I can hear a waterfall. Down there. That's definitely water.'

We continue on and his pace quickens. We arrive at rough steps that mark the descent into Waterfall Valley. The sun has set and twilight shrouds the campground. By the time we get the tent up, it's dark. I search for the candle lantern and light it while Chris inspects his big toe. The nail is ingrown and looks woeful. We had it looked at by a doctor when it first started playing up, but Chris refused to have it removed. He is sure he can live with it. He sponges it with tea-tree oil and assures me it doesn't hurt. He climbs into his sleeping bag and lays his head on a pillow he's manufactured from clothing shoved into a pillowslip.

'Oh,' he says, 'this is so comfortable. Let's not bother about dinner. I'm not hungry. Let's have it for breakfast.'

I pass him pieces of chocolate and a muesli bar.

'This tastes so good,' he says, swallowing mouthfuls of icy water from his drink bottle. 'Well, it doesn't taste of anything, which is what makes it so good.'

I blow out the candle and listen to him settle.

'Have a good sleep, Mum,' he says.

———

He wakes in time to see other walkers already setting off, heading deeper into the national park. I fire up the Coleman stove and we eat vac-packed lamb casserole and rehydrated vegies. I make a round of pancakes too. We pack our sleeping bags, deflate sleeping mats. We wash our dishes and then walk down to the stream to refill our water bottles. But as soon as Chris shoulders his pack, he loses confidence. We make it as far as the overnight hut, all of thirty metres away, and he dumps his pack on a table.

An older man, a volunteer doing maintenance on the hut, glances over at us and puts down his hammer.

'Need a hand with that pack?' he asks.

'Yeah,' Chris says. 'It's really uncomfortable.'

'Let's have a look.'

He has Chris put it back on. He tugs hard at the shoulder straps and gets some more height to the pack. He runs through the basics of a tight waistbelt and the importance of doing up the small strap across the chest. There's some advice that just comes better from a man when you're a thirteen-year-old boy.

'You've got an easy day today, anyway,' the man says. 'A pretty day.' He looks Chris in the eye and says, 'By the time you've finished this walk, you're going to feel like a million dollars.'

We head out on the track to Lake Windermere. Behind us, Barn Bluff stands dark red in the morning light. The sky is bright blue with thin white fluffy clouds to the south. It is already warm. Ravens wheel overhead and call from tree to tree. After wetlands, we begin ascending more wooden stairs and the heat bears down on us.

We take a break and Chris lies in the shade of a gnarly lichen-covered tree.

'I hate this walk,' he says. 'I'm not going any further.'

'Okay,' I say.

'Why did you bring me here?' he asks.

'Because you're my favourite camping companion.'

'Well, you made a mistake there.'

'Yes, everyone else is going to look like bliss after this,' I agree.

'I can't walk any further with this pack. I wouldn't mind if it wasn't so heavy.'

We sit. I see that the moment has come. Will he choose to go on? Will he summon some new part of himself that can do this walk?

'What are you letting run you right now?' I ask gently.

'Misery,' he replies.

'How does that feel?'

'Useful.'

—

Small insects with scarlet-tipped wings swirl about us. Fat mosquitoes, too, but they don't bite. Chris kills several in angry glee. The trees wait and breathe. I close my eyes and rest against a log. In the silence, a plane flies over.

I look up and say, 'Well, here's the rescue plane for you.'

He looks at me and says, 'Really?' He seems amazed and something else. What is it? Fear?

I smile. 'No.'

A few minutes later, he stands up and says, 'Oh, well, let's go.'

He shoulders his pack and begins walking. Soon he is fifty metres ahead of me. He stays that way for the next half-hour until we meet up at a stream where he's taken a break.

I say, 'Great walking.'

'Well, I just want to get there,' he says.

We are going forward and not back. Without the distraction of my concern for Chris, without the drone of his complaints, my own body begins whingeing. Hips, lower back. I am in awe that people ever crossed these sodden tangled high plains without the duckboards that ease our way.

We traverse a high mountain plain. It reminds me of a mesa in New Mexico, but instead of sagebrush there are stunted tea-trees blooming abundantly with small white flowers. The scale of the landscape is magnificent. In every direction there are rugged peaks, great scoops of valley, mountain ranges standing blue and distant, stacked one after another all the way west and south.

Halfway to our next campground, I have to stop and rest. I find a shady alley where I toss down my pack and open a bag of trail mix. Chris has found a walking stick of white tea-tree almost as tall as him and he is delighted.

'This makes it so much easier,' he says.

'My pack's so heavy,' I say. 'My shoulders are so sore.'

Chris tries in vain to find a walking stick for me, but none of the twisted limbs that scatter the ground or grow seemingly lifeless from the bare trees are suitable.

'Have mine,' he says, offering his prize.

'I'll be fine, sweetheart.'

'Well, just say if you need it,' he says.

—

We stop again near the turn-off to Lake Will. We lean back on black-and-white granite rocks and look out over rust-red moors and silver-white tarns. We try to identify all the peaks off the map, guessing where the track will take us.

'If you didn't have a pack, you could do this walk in a few days,' he says.

'Let's tell everyone it was easy,' I suggest.

He grins. 'I bet that's what everyone does.'

We descend to the black waters of Lake Windermere between huge shards of granite. Five hours after setting off from Waterfall Valley, our packs have become blocks of concrete. We drop them on the first empty tent platform and say very little for a few minutes.

In the humming afternoon heat, we pitch the tent. Some 4000 people walk the track each year. There is talk that soon the number of walkers will be limited. Tasmania grows ever more popular as a place of rare wild retreat.

We cook pancakes and eat them with strawberry jam. We make hot chocolate. The alpine gums surrounding the lake turn gold in the ageing day. Hard weather lingers on every crooked trunk and twisted branch. A breath of breeze arrives, cooling us. We have no idea if these warm days will continue. I lie down in the tent and soon I am snoozing.

It feels as if the whole year has finally caught up with me. I've been back at work in our advertising agency. I'd wanted to work from home a little longer with Elliotte still so young, but I was needed in the office. I miss my baby girl. I miss our days together in the flow of domestic life. But I've been called away by staff and clients, finances, phone calls, travel and community. I've employed the remarkable Iris, a nanny newly arrived in Tasmania, and Elliotte adores her. Still, it's been hard.

While I sleep, Chris whittles the end of his walking stick using a knife my dad has given him for this trip. When I wake, he is taking photos of the light along a ridge of hills. Away north, Barn Bluff's diminishing size marks our progress south. I can't help but feel that whoever named it rather undersold it. More insignificant landmarks and rock formations have earned the label Mount, but not Barn Bluff.

Chris is suddenly keen to cook dinner and we make chilli con carne together. The lake turns to pewter beside us. The dehydrated sweet potato cubes do not expand well. The peas do.

A pademelon emerges from the undergrowth and nibbles daintily at shrubs and roots just a metre away from us. It appears unfazed by our presence, and isn't expecting us to feed it. Three young men visit three young women on the next platform. Does romance take on a different quality out here? Is it infused by the bare high-altitude world, enriched by the proximity of water and sky, moss and damp earth?

In the tent, before we blow out the candle lantern, I read to Chris from *Love in the Time of Cholera* to make up for his missing book. I'm re-reading it for maybe the fifth time. Chris is immediately taken with the characters and pets, amused by the marital world. When I realise he's drifted off, I stop reading and listen to the night. After a few moments, a voice from a nearby tent says, 'Do you think you could keep reading?'

'Yes,' says another voice.

From another direction someone says, 'Five more minutes, please, Mum?'

'Please, Mum,' someone else adds.

There is giggling. I had no idea I had an audience.

'Okay, five more minutes,' I say to the invisible listeners.

———

In the night, possums attack the tent, trying to get to our food. It is a deliberate and concerted effort. At first, I push them away through the nylon, but they tear through the fabric. I am forced to use a metal drink bottle, full and heavy, as a weapon. Whacking them on their bodies has no effect. It is only when I smack their protruding snouts and hear the bottle clink on their gnawing teeth that they withdraw. Again and again, I am dragged from sleep to defend the tent. I wield my trusty silver weapon while Chris slumbers in oblivion beside me. I listen to his breathing and think of all the times he lay in my arms as a little person. It's a privilege to be allowed to sleep so close to him once more, this boy who is becoming a man, who will have less and less need of his mother in the years ahead. Parenting is a long lesson in letting go.

———

At dawn, one of the eighty species of birds in this alpine world honks like a klaxon and is answered by another bellow further down the valley. This goes on until I know there is no going back to sleep. Today we have a five-hour walk, although by now I know we travel at least two hours more slowly than the signed times. There are stops for water, for photographs, for gazing at the tiny worlds of moss and lichen, skinks and skats, for snacks and food, and for conversations that Chris likes to have when he finds a good log for us to sit upon.

He wakes and looks at me. 'I can't believe we're going to walk all day. Well, better get going. C'mon, Mum, hurry up.'

'My shoulders are so sore,' I say.

'What did I say before we started? This walk is a bad idea and we're going to be miserable.'

———

Setting out from Lake Windermere, Chris charges ahead. 'Imagine those guys who do Everest,' he calls back. 'They carry fifty kilos. But I guess they train for it every day.'

'The mountains are beautiful,' I say, staring at the skyline.

'They're okay,' he replies with a grin. 'We're making really good time. How far do you think we've come? How far to go?'

After the high moors, we reach the forest and leave the duckboards behind. Pools of golden light illuminate a carpet of fallen leaves. Soon it is wetter and steeper. We navigate long stretches of mud, stepping from stone to stone, grateful for the dead tree limbs previous walkers have laid across the path. The forest is dense with fronds, ferns and leaves brushing past us, the path corrugated with roots. We stumble, slip, tiptoe and skid for hours. We see nobody. I become a little concerned that we have somehow taken the wrong track, but at last we emerge at Frog Flats.

After a quick round of pancakes, we decide to go on to Pelion Hut, saving us a long day tomorrow. The walk proves easy and we arrive as the moon rises. After a dinner of rehydrated beef goulash and rice, we secure our tent as best we can from curious marsupials and head down to the river.

'Mum! Mum! Come and look at this wallaby. It has a tiny joey in it!' says Chris. 'Mum! Mum! Come and look at the river. Can we get across? I'm going to try. Come on, it's easy! There's just one hard bit. Isn't it amazing how our bodies know how far to jump and our feet go just the right distance and it's always right? Oh, look at this. It's beautiful!'

We sit on the pebble beach beside cascading water and talk about our plan for the following day. We agree we will sleep late. My legs are incredibly tired after the forest. Chris is impressed he has made the longest haul of the journey. He is wearing a blue beanie, his eyes full of the child he can't yet cover up. He giggles as he throws more stones to splash me and we play until it is almost too dark to see.

—

The sun is up and I am listening to the noises of tents being unzipped, the rattle of light metal breakfast bowls, the strike of match, the hush of fuel stoves, the frequent eruption of bird calls, the murmur of voices considering track times and lengths. I leave Chris to doze and sit beside the river rapids. Gone are the night animals. Gone is the pain in my hip to be replaced by a pain in my neck.

I close my eyes against the bright glare of sun and see images from the walk so far: eruptions of yellow grass, springs emerging from under the roots of trees, green-winged butterflies landing on our packs. I see fallen limbs grown soft and lush with pincushion mosses. I see a baby tiger snake with a bright yellow-striped underbelly.

The river lures me. I strip off and lie in the shallow water, dunk my head, splash my face. The pleasure of morning sun on my skin, the birds calling through this dappled forest – it is all so peaceful. I discover a grey rock covered in fossils at the river's edge and think of Byron and Elliotte. What sort of initiation might they need when they arrive at the threshold to adulthood? Will I walk this way with them when they are Chris's age?

I return to camp to make breakfast. Hungry, I imagine muesli, hot custard and soaked fruit. But the custard turns to glue as I cook it and Chris is grumpy. I am grumpy, too, because it is a special camping spot and we'd planned to spend the day by the river. I was going to read my book and rest but, now he's up, Chris is keen to move on. Pelion Gap at 1113 metres is in his sights.

'Why do you think we live with people?' I ask him.

'To learn to put up with things,' he replies.

—

By the time we set off, it's midday and hot. Other walkers are long gone. Twenty minutes up the track, we see a small path and hear water rushing. The river has divided, creating two waterfalls. Under one waterfall is a deep swimming hole. I strip off and dive in. It is cold but warmer than my early dip. It is bliss to feel weightless after the days of lugging a pack.

Until now, I've never given any thought to being naked around my kids. Chris and I have swum in all sorts of remote places. But today he resists a swim and I realise that, at thirteen, he's become shy. I remember being the same at his age. Instead, he asks me to say what sound I would like a rock to make when it hits the water. He is a piano player, like his dad, from a long line of piano players on that side of the family. I call out 'ker-thunk' or 'smack-plunk' or 'thwack-thwack' or 'spadoosh'. Chris chooses a rock, spins it or tosses it or catapults it into the air, and it lands in the pool making the requested sound. We laugh at this unexpected rock opera and our morning moods evaporate.

After dressing and snacking on trail mix and muesli bars, we begin the long walk up the ridge to Pelion Gap. We toil through lush rainforest, birds and insects making forest music, the canopy protecting us from another day of 25-degree heat. We cross a stream and Chris says, 'These little bridges are perfect for resting your pack.' He is right. If I surrender my urge to maintain momentum, I realise Chris's regular stops are good opportunities. He tells me about the storm on his recent outdoor education trip, when the thunder was so loud they couldn't shout over it. He tells me how they sat up all night on the beach watching the lightning overhead. I hear about the midnight walk he took with his dad, who still lives in Melbourne, and how they saw blue and green and gold bioluminescence in the water when they skipped stones. He tells me about the new house of his childhood friend in Melbourne and how his godfather's little boy has autism. He ponders the flecks in the rocks, and how he has seen several sorts of skinks on this trip and how many varieties are there? He talks of distances and terrain and which hills we are yet to climb. He wants fish and chips when we get home and I want pizza. A seafood pizza with lots of melted cheese.

We make Pelion Gap late in the afternoon. I shear the paper off the outside of the salami and slice cheese that is oily and delicious. Ants amass at Chris's feet as he drops cracker crumbs. Mount Ossa, snow-clad and steel blue, lies to the west. Pelion East on the other side of the pass is cloaked in rubble. Away north, Barn Bluff is a thumbnail now, reminding us how far we have come overland.

On the descent to Kia Ora, Chris calls out, 'Mum, come back! You've never see anything like it in your life.'

He's found an old piece of timber long buried at the side of the path. A natural spring has worn away a hole in the wood, and every few seconds water pumps from it as if it were a sprinkler.

'We'll never see it like this again,' he says. 'The stones will be different, the weather . . .' Just three days ago, he was having the worst time of his life. Now, here he is, imagining he might return.

—

The following morning is still and cloudless. We visit the old Du Cane Hut and Hartnett Falls. We meet a ranger on the track who tells us that in ten years he's never known the weather to be so settled and hot.

We are in rainforest again, giant widely spaced trees and gurgling streams cascading through broad lawns of moss. We cross Du Cane Pass at 1103 metres and begin a steep descent into Windy Ridge. By the time we arrive, my legs are like jelly. Stiff jelly. We make an early dinner then lie in the tent and I read more of *Love in the Time of Cholera* to Chris as evening falls. It is our last night. Tomorrow we have just nine kilometres to walk, all downhill.

He says, 'Can I watch as much TV as I like when we get home? Will you give me some money so I can buy a big packet of lollies? Can I stay up as late as I like?'

I say, 'Yes.'

He grins. 'You'll let me do anything now I've done this walk.'

'Well, I know you'll be able to do anything now you've done this walk. And you'll do it with grace and good humour.'

'I haven't done it with grace,' he says.

'Yes, you have. And an infected toenail.'

Through the open door of the tent, we watch a wallaby feed.

'Do you think wallabies think about things?' he asks.

—

We wake to the squawks, ululations, whistles and chirrups of birds. One last pack-up of camping bowls and sleeping bags.

One last round of gear stuffed into plastic bags. Grotty socks returned to our feet, smelly shirts and putrid shorts put back on our bodies, water bottles filled from a stream.

This whole year I felt as if I was missing out; preoccupied, occupied, too busy to sit on a log with my son. But I have stolen time to be with him. I have stolen nights to sleep beside him like we used to when he was little. I have stolen time away from other demands to hear him chat about weather and landscape, to muse on the lives and thoughts of animals, to laugh about mosquitoes and people, to trudge along and share complaints about the heaviness of our packs, the steepness of hills. We've rolled our eyes at track times and how nine and a half kilometres seems to take forever.

Have I prepared him for other walks? Has the trip inspired him? I am yet to know.

He takes all the heavy gear and puts it in his pack.

'Funny how you started out the strong one, but now it's me,' he says, his eyes twinkling.

Marching the last kilometre, we chant food names as we descend through forest – *ham-burgers, hot pies, chips 'n' sauce, chicken wings* . . . A few years back, we caught the launch up the lake. At the time I thought of Narcissus Hut as a dark, dank place. Arriving in the ringing heat of early afternoon, it seems the most cheerful place in the world.

The launch arrives to take us down the long lake to the lodge. When we arrive at the jetty, I watch Chris offer to help the boat captain heave all the packs off the boat.

'You've had a good trip,' the captain says to him as they work.

'Yeah,' says Chris, grinning.

172

We drink apple cider, clinking bottles as if it is beer. We eat the only hot food available at this hour – potato wedges with sour cream. The bus to take us home is an hour away. Chris strolls along the lodge verandah, easy, happy, taller somehow. He isn't a boy anymore, but though he isn't yet a man, I can see the man coming.

I realise I can let him go now. I can stop worrying about whether I've been a good enough mother, if I've given him enough. He *is* enough. He is more than enough. He has a whole life ahead, and whatever comes at him, he'll be okay. I have to trust that. He is older after this walk and, somehow, so am I.

FOREST

Never be afraid to tread the path alone. Know which
is your path and follow it wherever it may lead you; do
not feel you have to follow in someone else's footsteps.

EILEEN CADDY

It begins harmlessly enough. A poet asks me to help her place
a large advertisement in the newspaper. I run an advertising
agency, so that's easy. The ad contains an open letter to the
Premier of Tasmania pleading with him to stop clear-felling our
forests. They are not simply our environmental landscape, the
letter argues: they are our creative and cultural landscape, too.
Forty-five artists sign the letter, myself included.

The letter appears in the newspaper on the same day that
some 10,000 people march in Hobart to protest current forestry
practices – the kind of numbers unseen since the Save the
Franklin rally back in 1982 and the Sorry march for Indigenous
Australians some months before. The newspaper has been full
of articles and letters on the subject for the past year. It is a
hot issue.

My great-grandfather surveyed tracts of Tasmania's south-west. My family has been tramping about in these forests for generations. Now, every five minutes a log truck drives through the city carrying rainforest timbers to the woodchip mill.

Tasmanian forests were not being cleared to make money out of those timbers. They were being razed to make way for plantations of fast-growing, non-endemic pine and eucalypt species that could be harvested within fifteen years. Perfectly straight trees, previously the lifeblood of sawmills, went for chipping. The rest was incinerated. The rare and specialty timbers that woodworkers relied on for furniture-making were piled up and burned too. Many of those trees take hundreds of years to mature.

Both the federal and state governments were propping up the plantation push with tax breaks, incentives and subsidies. The government business responsible for clearing and replanting across the state, Forestry Tasmania, worked alongside a private company called Gunns Limited. Gunns had very close ties to both the Labor and Liberal parties. It had recently purchased the largest woodchip company in Tasmania.

—

One year after that letter appeared in the paper, I'm driving home from a morning run on a nearby beach. On a steep descent into the city, I come up behind a log truck carrying one enormous tree. It is seven or eight hundred years old. Logs destined for sawmills are marked with a metal plate. This rainforest giant has no plate. It's off to be chipped, like so many of its kin. Maybe it will become toilet paper or copy paper, chipboard or cardboard.

When I see the giant tree, it breaks my heart. I know its habitat. I know the entire ecosystem surrounding it has also been destroyed. Dry forests regenerate through fire, but Tasmania's wet forests do not. Once they are cleared and burned, they are gone. It's hard to imagine, if you haven't walked in rainforests, how lush, green, fecund, fragrant, musical and magnificent they are.

As the truck approaches the bottom of the hill, I think of swinging my four-wheel drive in front of it at the traffic lights. I'll refuse to move until something is done to stop this sense-less devastation.

Then I remember it is 6.30 am and I have three children at home who need their breakfast. I sigh loudly and continue on.

Later that morning, a journalist from the newspaper calls. She tells me the government has just announced the major sponsor for a new arts festival.

'Oh? Who is it?' I ask.

'Forestry Tasmania.'

I'm still reeling from the sight of the enormous tree that morning. I think back to the protest the previous year, the letter in the paper and the huge march through Hobart with 10,000 Tasmanians protesting current forest practices. This sponsorship of an arts festival is a very deliberate act. Everyone wants this new festival to succeed. Especially artists. So the government has concluded that it is a perfect opportunity to launder the image of Forestry Tasmania. It is an old trick in the world of adver-tising, and I'm not okay with it. So, I tell the journalist how I feel. The next day I am quoted on the front of the Saturday newspaper. The headline reads: SPITTING CHIPS ON ARTS DEAL.

As soon as I see my comments on the front page, I feel dread. My phone starts ringing. Other artists want to endorse my stand. They want to meet. We gather at our agency on the Sunday afternoon. We weigh options. We remind ourselves that over and again, opinion polls show 70 per cent of Tasmanians are opposed to old-growth logging and clear-felling. We decide to create a pledge campaign. Tasmanians can pledge to replace the money that Forestry Tasmania is offering the festival.

I have one novel to my name at the time. I am working on the second – *The Butterfly Man*. I have a husband, a two-year-old, a seven-year-old and a thirteen-year-old. I employ twelve people and more than fifty subcontractors. Seventy per cent of our business is government contracts. But I am a sun dancer. I danced for these forests. This tiny part of the world where I live has some of the most ancient remaining forests in the world. Am I going to stand by, or have I been called to take action?

The artists want me to speak on their behalf. The festival director is not Tasmanian, nor does she live in the state. It would be good if I went to speak with her. I am anxious about where this might go, how it might affect our business, my family, my employees. I don't like conflict.

On the Monday, I call and request a meeting with the festival director. I am told it is impossible. She will not speak with protesters. I am surprised. Isn't it an arts festival? Why would there be no conversation between fellow artists? No hearing our concerns?

I brief a designer, purchase a post office box and book newspaper space. The first pledge ad runs the following Saturday, the second a week after that. On the Monday after the second ad runs, I summon the courage to go to the post office. It is just across the road but I've been too nervous to see if anyone cares about our crazy pledge idea. I know there is community outrage about forestry, but will people put their money behind a protest?

As I approach the wall of letterboxes, I see a yellow slip poking out of our box. It reads: *Please come and get the rest of your mail at the front desk.*

The post office clerk hands me a large sack heavy with the mail, everything that couldn't fit in the box. What had we started? Hundreds and hundreds of people from all over the state had carefully cut out our ad and filled it in. Some pledges were fifty dollars, some a hundred. Lots of people pledged twenty dollars and many were for five or ten dollars. There were notes accompanying the pledges, saying things like: *I am Stacey and I'm ten years old. This is my pocket money. Please save the forests.* In envelope after envelope, Tasmanians had given what they could in order to replace the sponsorship of Forestry Tasmania. In ten days, we raise $51,455 in pledges.

Again, I call the festival office and request a meeting. The director's public response is vitriolic, but the general manager agrees to meet with us. She is clear. The festival will not accept the pledge money. It cannot set a precedent. If one sponsor becomes unacceptable, where is the line? Soon no company will be brave enough to sponsor the arts. She reiterates the director's position. We are tree huggers intent on destroying a new festival to further our own ends.

I explain that the pledges are from people of all ages, across Tasmania, wanting an end to clear-felling. I don't know their political leanings. It's a bigger fight than that. We don't want a fight with this festival. We want it to succeed. We want the arts to flourish in Tasmania, but not at the cost of our forests. We don't want Forestry Tasmania to be the major sponsor. If the government must use a government entity, why not give the money under Arts Tasmania? Parks and Wildlife? Why this choice?

The festival director writes me a letter insisting I take direct and named responsibility for the damage to the festival. She says we have misunderstood the nature of arts sponsorship in a most naive and dangerous way, causing extreme nervousness in other sponsors. Because we are writers and our books are published on paper, our position is ludicrous and hypocritical. We are nothing but a cowardly mob of ratbag greenies. The letter went on for five angry pages.

Most Tasmanians opposed to clear-felling were not aligned with green politics. They were worried about the effects plantations were having on our rivers and coastal regions. Chemicals flowing from plantations were already affecting oyster leases. Tasmanian devils, a marsupial found only on our island, were dying of a facial cancer linked to those chemicals. Plantations were often sited in water catchment areas, but the government had made no allowance for the effects on farmlands or reservoirs into the future.

Of all that the letter claimed and demanded, one sentence particularly unsettles me. It reads: *As this institution is as dear to my heart as old trees are to yours . . .*

How could a fledgling festival be compared to our wild forests? Besides, she had no idea how dear those trees were to my heart.

———

The newspaper asked me to write an essay. It was published one week and the festival director's essay was published the next. Some of her essay reprised her letter to me, although framed more gently. She incorrectly cited actor Peter Sellers for the quote: 'Sponsorship money is like sausage meat – it's best not to ask where it came from.'

Newspapers across Australia picked up the story. Back home, a swathe of letters from the public are published. Overwhelmingly, Tasmanians support the artists. Pledges continue to arrive. In twenty days, we've raised $75,000. More than eighty artists across Australia add their voice to our protest. I keep the festival informed, but there are no further discussions about replacing the Forestry Tasmania sponsorship. It is an absolute *no*. The premier calls us 'cultural fascists' in parliament.

———

I discreetly meet with people across government, politics and lobby groups both for and against current forestry practices. The facts are far from clear. There is much dispute about the direct and indirect jobs associated with Forestry Tasmania, the impact of poisons, the effect on water catchment areas, the financial modelling, the designation of 'old growth', the visual and environmental impact of clear-felling. I do not speak of these meetings publicly. I am doing my due diligence to ensure I'm not speaking from ignorance. The more I listen, read and learn, the more concerned I become that our irreplaceable forests are being destroyed for spurious short-term gain. Distant shareholders have no understanding of the damage caused by their investments.

The premier requests I attend an arts event. I am assured he is keen to be conciliatory. At the event, the premier publicly apologises for calling us 'cultural fascists'. He says, 'Although I may have been accused of inflammatory language, it was certainly not my intention to malign artists.' He will step down not long after this due to terminal illness and be replaced by his deputy premier, the minister for forestry.

—

A Sydney postcard company offers to run a national campaign for us. Pledge postcards fill the PO box. We have raised over $100,000.

I attend a large annual advertising conference in Sydney where a presentation is given on the *Discover Tasmania* Tourism Tasmania campaign. The audience is invited to ask questions. I ask if Tasmania's forest practices are having an effect on Tasmania's clean, green brand? At the next coffee break, the head of marketing for Tourism Tasmania rings me from Hobart. He wants to know if I have just asked a question at a conference in Sydney. He tells me it is in my interest to remain silent.

—

Together with a colleague, I create a billboard for Sydney airport with two photographs side by side. The headline is: DISCOVER TASMANIA BEFORE 2003. One picture is of ancient rainforest. The other is after it is logged. The caption reads: *Over 10,000 football fields of rare forest are clear-felled and burnt every year in Tasmania.*

Despite the advertisement being booked and paid for through a major media company, it is removed within four hours. The ABC quotes a Qantas spokeswoman saying pressure from the Tasmanian government has resulted in the billboard being taken down. Two days later, Qantas says that while the billboard didn't contravene their advertising policy, it was deemed a political statement. They also wished to correct an earlier statement – they had not been contacted by the Tasmanian government.

—

I am in the middle of a fight. I am a pipe carrier and I am being called to service. Every morning through the year leading up to the arts festival, I ask myself what I can do for the forests today.

The Tasmanian literary prize is one of the richest in the country and included in the program of the arts festival. Because of the artists' protest it is boycotted by prominent Australian writers. A Hobart gallery owner creates an alternative arts event to run parallel to the arts festival. It is called Future Perfect and Nobel laureate Günter Grass is its patron. Among its many contributors are acclaimed artists and writers, sculptors and media stars, a federal Labor MP, a famous senator and a leading economist.

—

At the launch of the new arts festival, the director declares the festival a success, our protest having made no difference. The following year, Gunns announces a pulp mill will be built on the Tamar River in northern Tasmania. The community

outrage comes hot and fast. Despite this, the federal government approves the pulp mill, even though the outflows into Bass
Strait threaten a vast tract of Tasmanian marine life. Gunns
sues twenty conservationists, including a federal senator, saying
activism has cost jobs and profits. They claim millions of dollars
in damages. It also emerges that a subsidiary of Gunns has
renovated the home of the premier to the tune of some $400,000
while the pulp mill was awaiting approval.

Our agency loses our government contracts. We hear we've
been blacklisted, but of course nothing is official. Seventy per
cent of our income disappears. I have to cut staff. They have
supported the protest, but it is devastating losing them, seeing
the impact on their partners and families. However, I've been
meeting with private industry clients, some of whom reached
out because of the protest, wanting to support our business.
We rebuild in the coming months, re-employ and rename,
partnering with a firm in New York and establishing ourselves
as Australia's first agency working with clients committed to
environmental and social wellbeing.

In 2009, *The River Wife* is published, a love story about a
man and a fish that I write in the rainforests of the Tasmanian
highlands. The Tasmanian literary prize is cut from $40,000 to
$25,000. By 2010 the woodchip market turns to cheaper plan-
tation fibre from South America and Asia. Forestry Tasmania
is unable to secure lucrative international accreditation due to
its environmental practices, and Tasmanian timber becomes
less appealing to overseas companies whose rigorous environmental standards are the benchmark. In 2012 Gunns goes into

voluntary receivership. Shareholders begin a multi-million-dollar lawsuit against the company.

—

In 2013 an historic peace deal – the Tasmanian Forests Agreement – is reached after four years of negotiation between various pro- and anti-forestry groups. It protects some 400,000 hectares of rare and ancient forest from clear-felling. It is an extraordinary truce between competing interests that sees the birth of unlikely friendships, a new respect between former adversaries and a healing in the Tasmanian community. After more than three decades of bitter fighting, an unfamiliar peace arrives. But still, hundreds of thousands of hectares have been cleared, firebombed and seeded with plantations whose value is in decline.

Despite the widespread relief in the community following the forest peace deal, the Liberal government that comes to power in 2014 tears up the Agreement. It attempts to push through anti-protest laws with fines of up to $100,000 for any protest that disrupts business operations or blocks access to worksites. Repeat offenders face a thirty-month jail sentence.

Forestry Tasmania rebrands in 2017 after it releases an annual report for 2015/16 announcing a $67.4 million loss. It is now called Sustainable Timber Tasmania. The 400,000 hectares protected by the Forests Agreement are once again slated for clear-felling. Native forests continue to be destroyed. The protest laws have almost been passed in the Tasmanian parliament.

—

Did it make any difference, our protest? It alerted other arts festivals to the challenges of sponsorship. Those concerns continue to this day. On a personal front, it was traumatising, something that only became evident as I wrote this essay. It's hard to fight for the rights of future generations to wander in magnificent old forests, to drink from unpolluted rivers, to breathe clean air, or to look up and see stars at night. It's hard to fight for species that have no voice other than how they speak to our hearts.

In Robin Wall Kimmerer's book *Braiding Sweetgrass*, she mentions that the Apache word for *land* is the same as the word for *mind*. If caring for the Earth is also tending to our minds, what might we grow, nurture, celebrate and protect?

DOLPHINS

How inappropriate to call this planet
Earth when it is clearly Ocean.

ARTHUR C. CLARKE

I've spent a fair bit of my life in the sea, so I've considered, from time to time, what I'd do if I saw a shark coming at me. One morning, swimming in a wetsuit with snorkel and goggles, I'm joined by something large, grey and sleek. When I see it slide in beside me, my first thought is: *big fish*. My next is: *dolphin*.

In Fiji I've dived with reef sharks and bronze whalers just metres away. I once swam with a large turtle off Fraser Island, holding on to its shell as it propelled me through the water. But I've never swum with a dolphin.

It is my regular swim from cliff to cliff at the beach where I live. I keep swimming, observing the dolphin through my mask. It stares back, regarding me with its large dark eye. We are close enough to touch but we don't. Then another dolphin drops in on my other side. Within a few moments, I am in the midst of six dolphins. Larger dolphins, smaller dolphins and one clearly a baby. I've kayaked beside dolphins and they are fast. To have them slow their pace to swim with me, they are choosing to accompany me.

I keep looking at them as I freestyle on. We swim a couple of hundred metres together. It is electrifying to be within their pod and peaceful. We are creatures of the sea together.

Then they begin swooping up and back through the water. I stop swimming to watch. They are leaping and arcing, flinging their bodies skywards and then diving back into the water beside me. It is early, the sea luminous, the air filled with rainbows in the spray from all this rising and diving. There isn't a cloud in the sky.

I think that maybe I am about to die. Maybe this is it. Something has come to get me. Maybe it's dolphins. Maybe the stars will start to fall. Maybe I'm leaving on a shower of rainbow light. If this is death, it's awesome!

I look back towards the beach, not sure what I will see. But the shore is still there. The houses and vehicles are still there. Two figures on the beach are watching. It doesn't seem like death.

I laugh and decide to keep swimming, imagining the dolphins will go off now and resume their dolphin lives. But they don't. They stop leaping and diving and rejoin me as I swim. We continue another hundred metres or so before they begin to peel away. Finally, only the first dolphin and the baby remain on either side of me. The baby is a little shorter than me. The parent, if it is the parent, is much larger. A taut, fluid creature continuing to regard me as we swim. Then the baby arcs away and the first dolphin follows, disappearing into the deep blue.

I put my head up and watch them swim away, leaping as they go. Soon they are fifty metres from me, then a hundred, then they are gone. I feel elated. I know it is unlikely this will ever happen again, but this magical thing *has* happened.

I complete my swim and come ashore, removing mask, snorkel and fins, then make my way back to the path. Two people are waiting for me. They are the couple who were watching from the beach. They say, 'You had an amazing time with those dolphins! It was incredible. We couldn't believe it!' It feels reassuring to know other people witnessed this moment. I have not imagined it.

———

In Indigenous culture, our interactions with nature have significance; they are signs to guide us or give insight into our world. I feel as if the dolphins came to acknowledge something. A beginning perhaps, or an ending. I don't know. But it feels precise. The experience resonates in me for days and weeks.

Less than a month after their appearance, my marriage ends. Adam and I were married in a ceremony comprising three traditions on a glorious summer afternoon in front of our friends and relatives. A sun dance brother came from America to marry us with a pipe. Mars, from the desert, gave us a tantric wedding blessing, and one of the Baptist brothers-in-law did a traditional Christian ceremony.

Over twenty-one years, we created so much together. There was travel and home, dinners and movies, music and art, work and children, and there was drama. The drama wore me out. I thought if I got better at anticipating it, it would become easier. But no matter how vigilant I learned to be, it never did. Marriage taught me to pay attention, to hone my instincts, to foster compassion, grace and kindness. I learned how hard fearless conversations are. I learned love can be created and re-created on a moment-by-moment basis. And no matter how good we make it look, love is not always healthy for the people involved. Sometimes the cost is too great. Sometimes the only way to grow is to complete commitments we thought were forever.

Reintegrating after that relationship would take me into five years of solitude. *The Museum of Modern Love* was published. I wrote *Bruny*. Chris moved to the United States, Byron finished a degree in Sydney, and Elliotte finished school and relocated to London for a working holiday.

I remain grateful for the years of shared life. But on the hard days, when the legal proceedings felt cruel, the friendship we once had eviscerated, I'd look out to sea and think about those dolphins appearing at that precise moment in time. Many people long to swim with dolphins. If my dolphin family returns, I'll wonder what will be required of me next.

ART

Beware; for I am fearless, and therefore powerful.

MARY SHELLEY

The film *Mary Shelley* undoes me. Elle Fanning is Mary pouring herself into her novel. Despite the social rejection of her unmarried status, the poverty of living with her lover Percy Bysshe Shelley, and the death of her first child, she writes *Frankenstein*.

In one scene, Percy sits by the fire in Switzerland with Lord Byron. Seeing those men in the security of their gender, the certainty of their brilliance, their elevated place in the world, I declare I will never love another artist. Where is the sort of love that doesn't require me to surrender some essential part of myself? A love that isn't jealous or cruel, competitive or fearful? Where the giving and receiving are both an invitation?

As the credits roll, I find the cinema bathroom and lean my head against the wall, weeping silently and inconsolably. I know what it is to write. I feel what it takes from me. What every writer gives up for it. The peace we will never have because of it. Rarely glimpsed between the covers of any novel is the love that was poured into every sentence. Every novel takes everything. *Every novel takes everything.*

We mother-writers, Mary Shelley and all of us before and since, we mother-writers must do this writing life differently. Our creativity cannot be corralled into a room of books where dust motes turn golden in the air. There is no time for writing when caring for children, submitting to the domestic routine: the appointments, the washing, the meals, the sick days, play dates and cupcakes for a class of thirty. We can't disappear for months researching in the streets of Belgrade or the deserts of Morocco, nor seclude ourselves behind closed doors for weeks on end. There is a generation of women coming who might make that happen. But, still, I imagine it will be a tussle, this balance of mothering, partnering, wife-ing, writing.

Some of us choose not to have children. Others find ourselves responsible for two, four, six . . . Doris Lessing had three but the first two she left with their father. She said, 'For a long time I felt I had done a very brave thing. There is nothing more boring for an intelligent woman than to spend endless amounts of time with small children. I felt I wasn't the best person to bring them up. I would have ended up as an alcoholic or a frustrated intellectual like my mother.'

Muriel Spark had one child but left him with his father. Fay Weldon had four. She once said of the work of her artist friends: 'What they've created is often better than the person, rather than the other way around.'

Unlike Doris Lessing, I found my children fascinating. They honed my discipline. Their presence reminded me time was going by, slipping away, life was moving on. Parenting requires generosity and stamina, two useful tools for the writing life. I loved the malleability, the moment-by-moment wonderings and wanderings of their minds, their ability to have fun in any circumstance. My children taught me to see the world anew every day. *Mum, do fish have dreams?* How we laughed. If I am lucky enough to know them, I'm sure my grandchildren will teach me, too.

Being a woman, mother or not, might be the greatest gift I have. My writing self has access to this empathetic, overstretched, nurturing, loving, fragile, courageous woman's heart. There are stories buried, camouflaged, in those tender places. For all the gifts being a man might bestow on me as a writer, I'll take this woman's life.

—

Going through a trunk of journals that date back to my late teens, I see my earnest scrawl written at the ends of days, on trains, on buses, in bed, by a fire, on a beach, in a moment when the inspiration came so hard I couldn't ignore it. Overheard conversations, dreams and threads, a vivid scene I witnessed or concocted in my mind. But often my journals contain questions. What happens after this? What happened before? What would she see? What sort of boat would he build? Can she forgive him? How do you blow up a bridge?

Within these journals are the beginnings of all my novels. There is an emotional intensity, an intellectual intensity, in the random collage of inspiration that makes me seem mad. I imagine carrying them to the beach and making a bonfire to burn away this inner life, to destroy this raw exposure, to liberate myself.

We writers are all duplicity, really. Mary Shelley created a monster to express her loneliness and abandonment. Stephen King created a mad nurse to express his addictions. I, too, have created worlds to contain parts of myself. Even I cannot be sure what is real or imagined by the time they are done, the characters formed, the world furnished and lit, the dialogue like scrimshaw whittled to some shape – not the rough bone of its beginning, but bone nevertheless. It is only much later, reading a fragment long after it is published, that I surprise myself with the candour I have given a subject, the clarity I have given a character. I have been hiding in plain sight, after all.

—

I need weather for writing. I once tried to write in the tropics but it was useless. My mind slumped. On this island, between mountain and river, weather is an incantation. I need summer's brief seduction, autumn's flamboyance, the steady blue of a winter sky, the moody, vain, euphoric temperament of spring. I love weather that glitters off the river as it ambles past, a sunrise that explodes, a racing moon. I love the barrage of an afternoon sea breeze, a gale that lifts the sea, thunder across the bay, and the hush of a rain-soaked world. Words are fragile. Like weather they come and go. Words take root in the places I know. From there I follow them into the places I do not.

Every story begins with a character. Every story is a radio playing in my head. If it cannot make itself known by way of pen, page or keyboard, it gets loud. Too loud. Since I was thirteen or fourteen, I've taken notebooks with me everywhere. I stopped a while back. For a month or so, I was without a blank-paged book. It was like losing the car keys. So, I started again.

—

I wrote seven of my novels mostly at night. I have given writing the fathomless hours of my life. It is a long road, learning a craft. Craft is the thing that brings me back, day after day, night after night. It is a vocation, this working against so many odds to become a better writer. I wrote my first novel at twenty-one, my second in my late twenties, but the third was the first to be published. I remember sitting on the front steps holding it in my hands, seeing my name on the cover of a book for the first time. It still surprises me with every book.

I started this writing life early, and yet now there are so few decades left. Every book demands more than I think I can give. This book has demanded more than any other. Every novel, every book, takes everything.

EAGLE

You're either suffering or you're having miracles.

BLACK JOURNAL, 2009

A couple of times each year, I go away with two girlfriends to different parts of Tasmania. We've known each other a long time and over three days we paint, eat, laugh and catch up on our lives. I'm a year into life beyond marriage and the whole year has felt like a coming to terms with the past. I am finding new ways to be.

When I realise where the house we've rented is this time, something stirs in me. I've never been back to Saltwater River, the place where Grandad and my brother Byron died.

I think about what I might do to honour the dead. My dead. How I might acknowledge the long road I have travelled since their deaths. I think about symbolic items, items from sun dancing, candles and flowers. I think about songs. But nothing feels right. Maybe I need to take nothing but myself.

On the last night of our stay, I say to Mary and Amy that there might be something I need to do tomorrow, something

I might need help with. I can't tell them what it is yet, and I'm not sure I'll be ready.

They say, 'No problem. Just let us know. If you want to do this thing, then we have all day.'

Such is the kindness of women.

When I wake, I realise it is a day for some kind of reckoning. I tell them my intention and they say, 'Cool.'

—

At 10 am we set off. As we drive, I am nervous, curious, happy and also a little sad. One day, forty years ago, Grandad, Nan and Byron came this way on a morning just like this. The sky is clear, the bay a calm green serenity.

I don't know the exact spot, so I wait for a sign. Was it here they parked the car, here where they went fishing? At an unmarked turn-off, my palms burn.

'Here,' I say.

We take a narrow dirt track to a shoreline of gum trees with sandstone ledges descending gently to the waterline. It's just the sort of place Nan and Grandad loved to picnic. I wander down to the shore. A raven, the biggest I've ever seen, takes off in front of me. It carves a straight course over the water. This is the place, I think. This is the place. This is the last shore they walked on, the last horizon they ever saw.

I don't know what I am meant to do, but a swim seems required. I put on my bathers and slip into the sea. This is where my brother and grandfather drowned. Here is the last water my brother felt against his skin. Here is the sea that enfolded my grandfather. I dive beneath the surface, rise and dive again, wanting to wash through and away the weight of the past.

It is a magnificent morning. The sea and sky seem to have made some happy arrangement to shine for each other alone. Other than my girlfriends on the shore, there is no-one else about. Summer is yet to arrive, and the water is cold. I float on my back and take in the sky. I feel as if the cold water is not actually touching me but is safely an inch away from my body. I close my eyes and let it infuse me.

I reach for some sense of Byron and Grandad. I imagine their drowning here. I think of the pain of water in the lungs, their panic, their fear. A chilling choppy sea, the boat upturned, the wind, and the words that pass between them. I can imagine all of it, and yet beyond whatever occurred, I can't feel anything unsettling or frightening or perturbing. It feels as if they departed life in an act of grace, surrendering to a hand or a wing that summoned them away. It devastated my family. It destroyed my mother. Yet all I can sense is this: the beauty and simplicity of life and death.

—

Mary and Amy are watching on, but I have slipped into a meditative space and forgotten all about them. What they see is a small breeze coming in from the north. It brings with it a cascade of rainbows across the water which wrap themselves around my floating form. I stay floating amid those rainbows, for almost an hour.

When I open my eyes and swim back to shore, a bird flies in over my head and settles in the tree above me. I am not quite ready to be in the world again and hardly give it a moment's thought. Some part of me is still in the water, in the mystery of it all. Mary wraps a towel around me. She whispers, 'It's a sea eagle,' and points up.

A white-bellied sea eagle is sitting on the branch above me. I gently raise my hand, as we do at sun dance, to acknowledge her. A minute later, she takes off across the bay. When she reaches the centre, she begins to circle, then slowly, majestically, spirals up. We watch her until the circle she is creating becomes so big she disappears.

—

Afterwards, we all remain silent. I do not get the shivers, despite the coldness of the water. I dress warmly and Mary makes hot tea. I go to sit on the shore alone. I want to write about this experience, so it won't leave me.

As I am writing, it occurs to me that nothing bad happened here. Despite the pain it caused my family, the fact that Byron was so young, that Grandad died with his grandson, that they both drowned, it feels like nothing bad happened here. For Grandad, for Byron, it was *what happened*.

Then it occurs to me that nothing bad ever happens here. Every human life is perfect in its own way. We cannot understand that, because it seems like there is so much suffering. But every life is perfect for what we need to know and learn and see and understand. Even when we don't understand, even when the suffering seems unfathomable, does some part of us understand? Could that really be true? I want to resist it. I think of the most horrific circumstances which are clearly bad and wrong, but over and again I hear those words:

Nothing bad ever happens here.

My body starts shaking then. It is not some delayed reaction from the cold. It is the reverse of all those years ago in the desert when that figure walked towards me from the sun and electrified me. There on the rocks at Lime Bay, something is pulling me out of my body, a reverse lightning bolt trying to fling me to the heavens. I dig my fingers under the rock I am sitting on. I resist that force with all my might. I am not having another weird spiritual experience. I remember all too well what happened after the desert. What happened to my mind and what happened to my world. I can't go through that again.

Nothing bad ever happens here.

The force is tugging as hard as a game fish on a line. Damn it, I think, I like this messy, crazy, unexpectedly beautiful and wonderful havoc that is life. The bright, whimsical, practical, time-borne existence that is perfect in every way. It's perfect for each and every one of us, no matter how crazy that seems in the wild quantum of human experience.

Nothing bad ever happens here.

I hold on to the rock beneath me as if I am clinging to life itself. Maybe I am. I cling to this life, my life. I don't want to go anywhere. I don't know the truth about anything for sure, but I know I like being unevolved. I like not knowing. I like being unenlightened. I like this human life with its fast bikes and rock 'n' roll. With its Mustangs and buffalo. Its dancers and dreamers. Children and clouds. Bourbon and pizza. I like the ordinariness of it all. The ordinary is the extraordinary in a human life. Extraordinary things happen to ordinary people every day – if you're paying attention.

We might be entirely comprised of atoms, the 5 per cent of the universe we know about, but I'm convinced we surf the unknown 95 per cent. It's within us, around us, in every-thing. No wonder we feel like there is something more to life. Whatever a life is – an organic or a cosmic experience, it's also both things. Organic and cosmic. We love the paradigm but what matters is that we are part of 100 per cent. We are all part of a whole, connected and affected by one another and the energy we cannot see. *Mitakuye oyasin.*

This world is both chaos and peace. There is force and power. Direction and intention. Movement and stillness. Light and also shadow.

When death takes my hand, I want to know I've lived with every sense and awareness, applied every power in me to live wholly and fully. I want to take this great gift of life and run as far as I can in my unevolved state. No matter how far the dead go beyond the sea and sky of this world, they remain our challenge and our blessing.

The shaking settles. My body stills. I am here on Lime Bay and, despite the stories of my family, it is so beautiful.

Nothing bad ever happens here.

—

Two years later, I'm at a spiritual retreat in Queensland. I've been here a week and every day we meditate a little longer. We are playing with increasing our energy. If all our wildest dreams come true, how would we feel? How would that delight, that abundance, that life feel? The art of this meditation is to hold that feeling and draw the future towards us, playing with creation, and having it play with us.

In preparation for the next meditation, I'm doing a walking meditation on a playing field. Without warning, my brother Byron appears in front of me. It gives me such a fright, I drop to my knees. He smiles at me, that same smile I remember so well. He is a man, his hair with a little grey, his eyes still blue. He is transparent, as usual, but unmistakably my brother.

He says to me, 'I died so you would know two things. To never be afraid of death. And to live every day.'

Once again the wound of grief breaks open. I surrender to the place in my heart that has held all this for so long. I weep. He is right, of course. He twice appeared to me after he died, smiling at me, silently reassuring me. I've never been frightened or worried about death because of those two appearances. I knew something existed beyond this life because my brother came to visit, and he was smiling.

I'd learned from Pa's death, and then Byron's and Grandad's, that death could happen at the most unlikely, unexpected moments. It could wreak havoc on everything that appeared stable and certain. I had set about making sure I lived. I chose life over and over again. I chose to live with my heart open, my eyes open, my mind open to all the beauty, the possibilities, knowing the risks and fears, not always understanding, but following the calls that came and the mysteries that unfolded. Even when I was in pain, through love and loss, good days and hard days, the challenges of parenting and working, love and despair, all the demands of a creative life, I've made the most of every moment.

The sacred wound of grief received by my twelve-year-old self has been one of my greatest teachers. Chronic pain has been one of my greatest teachers. There is choice. We can suffer or make miracles.

Our bodies remember the past perhaps more than our brains. It takes everything to forget. Putting the past aside to focus on now, on this moment, is a victory. Every time we are here, in the vivid now, with breath and eyes, smell and touch, is a victory. It isn't that the past didn't happen. It isn't that we must forgive or forget, although we can. There are lives we might have lived, could have lived, didn't live, and this one we are living right now.

It's good here. It's good it's now. I'm so glad it's now.

ELEPHANT

Wear your heart on your skin in this life

SYLVIA PLATH

This is the elephant in the room. It's the bit that joins most everything together, yet it's the bit I least want to talk about. But here it is. The whole elephant.

The rheumatologist who diagnosed me at twenty-one was right: the flares did worsen. And I did everything I could to keep them at bay.

Chronic pain is not like the pain of a broken arm, a burn or a wound. Acute pain is short-lived in the grand scheme of things. My body is peppered with scars large and small. I've been reckless, lawless, careless, fearless and breathless, and I've loved every minute of it.

—

Ankylosing spondylitis is not the osteoarthritis of older people, and it's not rheumatoid arthritis. It's an arthritis that cripples me for weeks and months, flaring suddenly, inflaming ligaments, muscles and joints. Flares have come from climbing a step, twisting to reach something, lifting or moving something heavy, or from a fall. Flares have come on after a bushwalk the day before, or a night of dancing. Sometimes they've come with a period of emotional stress or erratic weather. Sometimes from doing something as simple as bending while cleaning my teeth. Sometimes they emerge after a week or two of being haphazard with my diet. If two or three factors collide, I will go down fast. But not always. Not predictably. It's always random.

What is not random is what happens once the flare begins. Within an hour or two, I am immobilised. My bones feel as if they're on fire. That's why it's called a flare. With the pain comes nausea. There is a weird sense of being eaten away from the inside, gouged out, sucked dry. I wilt under the weight of this cellular war.

—

'What did I do wrong?' is always the first question I ask myself when a flare-up begins. What did I do wrong? What could I have done to avoid this? Why now? Why this?

My friend Mark, who died of motor neurone disease, would ask himself the same questions. I know people who lost loved ones to suicide and they ask themselves these questions too. What did I do wrong? What could I have done to avoid this? Why this? Why me? Why now?

—

Having a chronic condition is not akin to death. It's like living with a house guest who never leaves. Sometimes they mess the place up big time. They make chaos out of order. They wreck your plans, cancel your holiday, reorganise your social life, ruin your job prospects, interrupt your sex life and spend your time and money on endless appointments and a cupboard full of pharmaceuticals, vitamins and supplements. Other times, they retreat to their room, sometimes for months on end. But they do not leave.

The dying usually want more time. People with chronic pain want more time without pain. Both seem reasonable requests. But both seem born of a failure to understand and accept that the human body is both finite and flawed. Some of us die young, some very young, many die before their time (as we like to say) and many, many people suffer every day from things that will never kill them, but might kill their joy for life. Even talking about pain feels treacherous. If I don't talk about it, perhaps it won't happen. Perhaps it will stay away and not return.

In Western society we now attempt to ensure the dying do not suffer. But what if we suffer as we live? Perhaps those who live with daily pain are the only ones who can learn not to fear it.

—

I hate pain. I want to be rid of it. I fear its onset. I rail at its voice. I weary of its persistence. But chronic pain hasn't killed me. It won't kill me.

Every day I want it gone. I have lived for weeks and months and years in severe pain. One day, while driving, I heard people on the radio talking about their chronic pain and I had to pull over to the side of the road and weep. They told stories of searing, breathtaking, crippling, vicious, ugly, defeating, seemingly pointless pain. People living through breakfast, through work, through dreams and birthdays, hopes and surprises, children, love and disaster, all in terrible pain. I look back at family photos and I can tell by the cast in my eyes, or my smile, how much pain I was in at that particular moment.

On the good days, I'm able to subdue the pain almost to zero. Meditation and mindfulness taught me to do that. I take a selection of drugs and supplements to help with this, too, but my state of mind is paramount. I have learned to use my mind to turn down the pain so regular day-to-day life is possible, but if you prod me on any joint where tendons attach – my hips, coccyx, my fingers (most of my bones, actually) – then the pain is there. Beneath my mental control, my body is always sore.

If you want to shake my hand, please do so gently. I can't tell you how many men have grasped my hand and caused it to ring with pain for minutes. Of course, they would never know it. I am the queen of smiling through.

—

It's hard to imagine the pain if you haven't ever felt it. Years ago, I broke my foot. I fell into an outdoor bath in the dark at 3 am after a night of very good food and wine. I saw stars. There was a major hospital an hour and a half away, but a small hospital just twenty minutes away opened at 7 am. Adam slept while I waited through the night. He was sure it was a sprain.

By the time I got to the waiting room, I was using all my focus just to breathe. When they X-rayed my foot, they discovered a spiral fracture the length of the fourth metatarsal.

'You seem so calm,' the nurse said. 'It must be very painful.'

'It is,' I said. It was excruciating. I did not add that acute pain is easier to bear than chronic pain. Acute pain is straight-forward. It has a scale of one to ten. There will be an end point. It will stop.

Chronic pain is different. Chronic pain has no end in sight. No-one can take the pain away and give me back my life. I have to wait. On a scale of one to ten, ankylosing pain interrupts daily life at six out of ten. I dread the stairs to the bedrooms. The stairs to the washing line. Drawers I must bend to open, a bed I can't make, a dishwasher I can neither stack nor unstack. It's impossible to reach down for something I've dropped, to pat the cat or pick up a toddler.

At seven out of ten, the pain is compelling. I go to bed. I cancel anything planned for the coming week because I know I won't be back in the world for a while. I increase pain relief and lose my appetite. Waves of nausea wash through me, dousing me in sweat if I try to stand for more than a few minutes. I don't vomit. The pain of all those muscles tensing would be indescribable. With seven-out-of-ten pain, I can't drive the car. I can't get in the car. I can't sit; I have to stand or lie down. I'm too tired to watch a TV show or a movie.

At eight out of ten, it's hard to hold a conversation. It's hard to breathe. Hard to read. Very hard to move. People are too loud. Everything is too loud. I can't stand in the shower. I can't bear anyone to sit on the bed because even the tiniest move-ment is agony.

Beyond ten, a flare has a scale of colours. There is red pain and yellow pain, purple pain and blue pain, and there is the white pain of complete and utter surrender – or maybe defeat. It's the world of four-hourly morphine, a drug that takes away all my personality, all my joy, numbing me entirely. I am gone into a grey nothingness. I can barely wake, barely speak. It is a truly awful medication to rely on. Depression lives right there.

At some point, a flare lets go. Weeks later. Months later. One flare continued for four years. For those four years, I was on varying concoctions of opioids, steroids and strong anti-inflammatories every day. When I took myself off the opioids, desperate to feel clean at any cost, I had days of teeth-chattering sweats, muscle cramps, body aches and tremors like a true addict.

Through all this, during my thirties and forties, I was a mother, a wife, a friend, a business owner, a daughter. I was chair of our agency network, chair of a festival. I sat on various boards. I looked after people I loved. I had that fight with the government. I taught writing. I coached my children's hockey teams. I swam, walked, danced, held dinner parties and wrote novels. During some of the worst years, I began a children's series with my friend Danielle Wood. We wrote the Tuesday McGillycuddy books for middle-grade readers under the pen name Angelica Banks. They were published internationally.

—

Every day I'm not in pain, I'm grateful. I'm grateful I can walk. I'm grateful I can do the shopping or attend appointments. I can live what most people think of as a normal life.

I've learned to be grateful on the days I'm in pain, too. I'm grateful for clouds that pass my bedroom window in seemingly effortless new designs, constantly rearranging themselves so I am never bored. I'm grateful for drugs that dull the edge, settle the symptoms, take the sting away. I'm grateful for whoever spent their life developing the drugs and thought to search for a cure for people like me.

I'm grateful for the kindness of my children, who continue to love me and smile at me, to make me tea and juices, to hand me my walking sticks through the ups and downs of flares. I'm grateful for the girlfriends who bring meals and, when the children were small, did some of the running around and domestic chores.

I'm grateful my rheumatologist has made this condition one of her life's projects, conducting research trials and expanding medical knowledge on women with this condition. I'm grateful for the friends who do not look at me as if I have a spiritual, emotional or psychological issue to resolve whenever I cannot walk. They remind me that there is life beyond this time and, when I return, I'll be no less loved or respected, and always welcome.

—

When the pain lets go, I can do so much. But if the pain is there, everything is hard. Often, I give no indication of this. Clients and colleagues call, not realising I am in bed. 'How are you?' they ask. 'Great,' I reply, looking down at my pyjamas. It's so much easier to say that one word than launch into an explanation or deal with sympathy.

I've conducted interviews, attended literary events and looked to all the world as if I'm glowing, until friends have helped me away afterwards. On those occasions, my children call me Meryl. They say I could win an Oscar for looking fine when I'm not.

Pain has carved me almost all my life. I can't see what it's created, but whatever it is, it's hard won. I suspect it is for anyone living with physical limitations or chronic pain.

Sometimes friends ask, 'Don't you think you should slow down? Aren't you doing too much?' But distraction is helpful. Lingering in the world of suffering is unhelpful. I'm not suffering. I'm living, albeit in pain, like so many people do.

———

Eventually a day comes when I move a little more freely and feel a fraction better. This is the day I feel sorry for myself. *Why me? Why this?* the voice in my head begins, and I know I'm on the road to recovery. When I am truly unwell there is no energy for self-pity.

I begin to stretch out and straighten up. I am tired, but a seed of buoyancy is taking root. The nausea abates, the gnawing worm of ill health recedes, the burning pain in my joints dulls, the fatigue slips from my limbs, the heaviness lifts from my shoulders, the strain departs from my face, the hollowness leaves my eyes.

It is a tentative process, recovering from intense pain. It feels enormous to venture back into a world that has continued on without me. Everything after a flare-up is fast, noisy, demanding, tiring. Sometimes it takes weeks for my body to find ease and flow. I am desperate to avoid anything that might trigger a relapse.

———

In recent years, medical cannabis has brought blissful relief. I can still have conversations, sleep deeply, laugh and have creative thoughts. I can write. I may not be able to walk around, or drive the car, but I am still me. Still happy, curious, optimistic, loving, grateful. I'm no longer forced to lose myself in a dark, opioid abyss for relief. Medical cannabis is the most effective pain relief I've ever known. There have been endless studies showing its therapeutic value for a range of diseases and conditions. In Australia it's still barely legal and difficult to acquire, while in the US, the UK and many other countries, it's been available over the counter for years. This infuriates me.

———

Consider these two words: *in*valid and in*valid*. One refers to being weak, sickly, too ill to care for oneself. The other means not valid, unable to perform active service.

When I am bed-bound, pain ridicules my dreams. I love my life. I have people to care for and things I want to contribute. I love being able-bodied. But if illness robs me of all that, does that make me in*valid*? Who needs a sick wife, a sick friend, a sick mother? What sort of a role model am I? She with the fragile body and bathroom drawers full of pills.

Very few people ever see me on walking sticks. I simply retreat. I do not want anyone to think of me as my illness. I'm ashamed of the pain. I do not want anyone to see how I have failed again at being well. I have held back tears, smiled and summoned joy rather than convey to another human, even some of those closest to me, how tough things were at the time. If people only see the vibrant, energetic Heather, they will think that is the real me, the *valid me*. Over time, I take a good long look at shame, at the notion of being *an invalid*, and I begin to see ankylosing spondylitis as a hallowing presence.

—

People meditate on their tumours and find them gone. They cure themselves of incurable conditions. I've done the affirmations, practised the magical thinking. I've tried the remedies, diets, rituals, meditations and mantras. I've listened to the gurus, drunk the juices, read the books. I've searched my soul for any aspect that might harbour some enjoyment of the pain or might secretly benefit from a life limited by illness.

I've had many people in my life look at me as a potential miracle. 'What do you think you need to learn from this?' they ask. 'Do you really want to be well? Have you visualised yourself well? What's stopping you from being free of illness? Do you really want it gone? Have you read Louise Hay? What about Eckhart Tolle, Thomas Moore, Osho, Black Elk, Louise Erdrich, Marianne Williamson, Wayne Dyer, John Bradshaw, Brené Brown, Paramahansa Yogananda, Brandon Bays, the Dalai Lama, Thich Nhat Hanh, Martha Beck, Byron Katie, Dr Joe Dispenza?'

These questions are usually asked with kindness, yet they feel patronising. They often come from people who have rarely had a sick day in their lives. To them, my illness implies something faulty with my mind, my spiritual development or my character. Surely if I think myself well, in just the right way, I'll heal myself?

My brother once told me that if I took the Lord Jesus Christ as my Saviour, I'd instantly be well. I see that it's hard to know what to say to a person with a chronic condition. 'Bad luck!' might suffice, if it had anything to do with luck. Or, 'Glad it isn't me,' which is what everyone is thinking but not saying, just as we do at funerals.

Just in case you've got suggestions: here's a quick list of the therapies I can recall trying over the past forty years: rheumatology, physiotherapy, osteopathy, naturopathy, chiropractic, craniosacral therapy, massage therapy, Bowen therapy, gastroenterology, pharmacology, psychology, pain management, bodywork, structural realignment, homeopathy, vitamins, mineral salts, rebirthing, MORA therapy, acupuncture, Chinese herbs, juices, spirulina, ionic silver, prebiotics, probiotics, primal therapy, grief counselling, chakra breathing, reiki, tantra, float tanks, Kundalini work, Buddhist meditation, New Age meditation, neurolinguistic programming, kinesiology, journey work, women's circles, crystals, past-life regression, initiatory rituals, vision quests, deep earth ecology, sweat lodges, Bach flowers, labyrinths, shiatsu, art therapy, structural mechanics.

My body has been treated, touched, adjusted, manipulated, balanced, invigorated, restored, mobilised, medicated, analysed, tested, detoxified, cleansed, dieted and diagnosed. There have been any number of food regimes. No starch, low starch, paleo, candida elimination, vegetarian, vegan, no fruit, no sugar, no saturated fats, no red meat, raw food, the fast diet. Sometimes they made me feel fabulous. Sometimes just hungry. And always, at some point, there is another flare.

—

When a flare returns, these are my questions:
    What triggered this?
    Why is it happening this time?
    What do I need to learn?
    What limiting beliefs do I have to look at this time?
    Do I really love myself?
    Can I love myself like this?
    What help do I need?
    What does my body need?
    My heart?
    My soul?

—

What benefit could there possibly be to all this suffering? Will it make me a better person, friend, writer? If I could swap any benefits to live without pain, would I? Yes. And no.

I would not want to give up the compassion I have learned for the suffering of others. I would not want to give up the insights I've gained into health, love, kindness, friendship, depression and joy. But if I could choose right now to be well and never troubled by this pain again? Yes. Yes. Yes. A thousand times yes.

—

Bring me fish and vegetables. Check in from time to time but don't expect a prompt reply. Ensure the house is quiet so I can sleep. Change my bed linen. Empty my bins. Fill my water jug. Take out the rubbish. Do anything that requires lifting or bending or carrying. Run me a bath or help me shower. Bring me clean pyjamas. Help me to dry myself. Check I have the right drugs on board. Check my calendar and cancel things for me. Cover for me. Remind me I'm loved. Touch me very gently. Remind me that this, too, shall pass. Help me to sit in the sunshine. Be compassionate. Once the worst has passed, bring champagne and oysters. Bring good red wine and a movie. Laugh with me. Do not feel sorry for me. Do not pity me. Do not talk about your own pain or a remedy you've just heard of that's sure to work for me. Most of all, see me as whole, because inside, I still am. Have no fear for me, or yourself.

—

Not long ago, I discovered both my parents carry the genetic marker for AS. It's related to Crohn's disease, irritable bowel syndrome, kidney problems, iritis, gut problems, sleep disorders . . . and early-onset heart disease.

My father had his first triple bypass at fifty-nine. One of his brothers at thirty-six. His oldest brother died from a heart attack at forty-two. On the other side of the family, Grandad Burgess had his first heart attack in his early forties and five more before he died at sixty-seven. Like Grandad, like my dad, I was active, ate carefully, drank little, didn't smoke, didn't carry extra weight. But heart problems came along in my late forties.

We each live with a beating heart. That rhythm is so familiar, we rarely notice it. But when it goes wrong, when that rhythm changes, when inflammation happens in the heart lining, when spasms occur, the body goes into high alert. It demands immediate and precise focus.

Heart inflammation can also take weeks to settle down. There's not very much research on the connection between inflammatory arthritis and heart disease, especially not in women. Women's hormones interfere with research models. Our symptoms are different, too, and most doctors have not been educated to look for them.

The research of developmental biologist Bruce Lipton indicates our genes and DNA do not cause illness. Illness is a response to environmental and emotional factors. I do not dismiss my emotional landscape. Bessel van der Kolk writes on the long-term effects of trauma in his book *The Body Keeps The Score*. AS symptoms started around the time my brother and grandfather died. The disease worsened after malaria. I spent eight years on serious anti-inflammatories. At the end of those eight years, the drug manufacturer announced that the drug could cause heart damage if used for more than four months.

—

Buddhist rule number one: *All of life is suffering.* I don't mean to correct the Buddha, but I would like to reframe that truth slightly: *Some of life is suffering.* Some days will be hard days. Some days our hearts will be broken. Some days our spirits. Some days our bodies will be fragile, thin-skinned, prone to disease and in need of restoration that requires more sleep than we've made time for. What if we accepted suffering not as a sign that something is wrong but a sign something is right? A reminder that we are human?

We are not yet the super-creatures, the avatars of our computer games. We are cellular. We have systems and cycles. We are vulnerable to the weather, the moon cycles, the food we eat and the air we breathe. We are vulnerable to chemicals, education and religion. We are vulnerable to alcohol, drugs, radiation and pollution. We are vulnerable to social media and the devices we hold in our hands. We are living on a planet in crisis. Mental illness is an epidemic in our young people.

I have dear friends who suffer from mental illnesses. They too have flares. Their minds go to places that they cannot come back from without medication, time and healing. Observing this, I have learned that mental illness is just another chronic condition and requires the same tender care and kindness, the same lack of judgement. We are all doing the best we can. Experiences are not simple. Suffering is not simple.

—

A friend who has almost never been ill, seeing me in need of pain relief, tells me I am a drug addict.

'Of course I am,' I agree. 'Anyone with chronic pain is. Just as people with mental health issues are. We require our medication to attempt to lead a normal life.'

It's an important distinction. There are people who seek to escape life through drug addiction. Then there are those of us who need medication to be present in life. Maybe we are less *addicted* than *reliant*. We rely on the sanity and salve medication provides for us.

—

In my early fifties, I begin to get well. After my marriage ends, I rest. Life becomes peaceful. The house is quiet and I sleep undisturbed. It feels as if it takes three years to catch up on all the sleep my body needs. I start meditating for an hour or two each day as I manage the tsunami of emotions all the changes bring. Divorce is such a shift in identity. The emotional terrain is tough, but the physical pain subsides radically. Wellness becomes almost reliable.

For four years, my body loosens up. The habitual stiffness and soreness dwindles. I have setbacks. One Christmas, I have a nasty flare, one of the worst in the past decade. The pain is breathtakingly savage. My body has forgotten how all-consuming pain can be.

Byron is home on holiday and he stays until I can walk again. No-one is angry or annoyed that I am ill, or that plans have been upended.

Medical marijuana makes the journey as soft as possible. Within two weeks I suggest to Byron that I'd like to take a little walk outside. 'But it's too hard to get dressed,' I say.

'Wear your pyjamas,' he suggests.

'I can't do that,' I reply.

'Yes you can,' he says. 'I'll wear mine, too.'

So, I walk the path by the beach, a walking stick on one side and Byron on the other. The next day we go a little further. Eventually the stick disappears. One day we even get dressed.

'You're so tantalising with your ankylosing,' Byron quips, as we have a gentle dance in the kitchen.

—

Biologics are a relatively new approach – a serum that has to be injected weekly, fortnightly or monthly. These injections have been very successful. I extend my gratitude to all the laboratory rats who have suffered and died bringing me this chance of health. It's an enormous gift.

Women do not have the same inflammatory markers as men, and unlike men our joints do not fuse but continue flaring, so without supportive doctors, some women are ineligible for the government subsidies that bring the cost of these injections down from thousands of dollars to under fifty dollars. This approach appears more interested in allowing people, especially women, to become disabled, rather than helping them ahead of debilitation to remain functional, tax-paying contributors. We have a long way to go in our healthcare system.

Anecdotally, some women report they had no more flares after menopause, but there has been no research into that. If it were true, what might we do medically? How might we save women years of pain?

—

Apparently AS people have an 80 per cent chance of becoming clinically depressed. I've had to resist that rabbit hole with every fibre of my being. Whatever came at me, I saw the choice between falling into a belief that the world would be better off without me, or choosing love, joy and connection.

Do joy and pain have an inverse relationship? The more pain I feel, the less joy is possible. And the reverse is true. The more joy I feel, the harder it is for pain to gain a foothold. Joy is an act of courage. At any time, illness might return. It might all go wrong. I elevate my emotional wellbeing every day through meditation. We've spent a century learning about healing our emotions, but what about emotions that can heal us? Social researcher Brené Brown discovered that courage requires vulnerability. Is courage also at the heart of healing?

I know I'm lucky to be able to manage my emotional health. But to everyone who doesn't, and can't, you have my love and compassion. I know eventually I'll get well again. And every time I do, especially now I'm older, I think: *That's the last time. Never again.* I am an eternal optimist.

—

In his book *The Art of Living*, the Buddhist monk and teacher Thich Nhat Hanh wrote: 'We should not be afraid of suffering. We should be afraid of only one thing, and that is not knowing how to deal with our suffering. Handling our suffering is an art. If we know how to suffer, we suffer much less, and we're no longer afraid of being overwhelmed by the suffering inside.'

—

In the middle of winter, I begin swimming in the sea without a wetsuit. After four years of wellness, I've been bouncing between arthritis flares and heart flares for months. The water is about

10 degrees. Some days I have angina, high blood pressure or joint pain, but I go in anyway. The angina doesn't worsen, nor the blood pressure, and the joint pain is always eased by floating. After half an hour of gentle swimming, I get into a 40-degree magnesium spa to warm up again.

Elliotte is home from London. She cares for me through the year as I oscillate between good days and hard days. I am touched to see her grown into a woman capable of such enormous kindness and empathy.

I begin a new program of injections. They do not cause the nasty side effects I've experienced with previous injections. I begin to get fit again. The pain in my joints subsides. Health returns. Pain still wakes me in the night, but mostly it's gone by mid-morning. My heart is unpredictable, but I'm carefully medicated. I have wonderful specialists.

Lots of people my age are slowing down, groaning as they rise from the couch, sighing when they get into bed. Some of them are getting osteoarthritis or rheumatoid arthritis. They are surprised by the pain. I feel as if I've had my old age early. Often, I appear younger and healthier than my peers. I've had to think about wellbeing for decades whereas other people my age are just beginning.

What I know is that illness has heightened the magic of life. Joy is my daily practice. Joy is my discipline. Joy is as essential as food, water, any diet, supplement or regime. Joy is an invitation to health. Joy is flow.

I take nothing for granted. Not the act of walking, or my heart beating quietly in my body. I'm grateful for all I have and for everyone I love. I'm grateful for all the experiences along the way. I try to stay on good terms with all human beings. I take nothing for granted. We are all on the road to death.

Are there clues to wellness I am yet to discover? I'm sure there are. We don't know the answers to healing, but there are people suffering every day with all sorts of chronic pain. So, I'll keep looking for answers.

GARDEN

When life seems most impossible
Surrender to the possibility that everything
Absolutely everything
You've been through has been utterly necessary
To get you to now
To love.

TINA CHRISTENSEN

I've only ever fallen in love, with true and precise awareness, once. The day before, in an airport, I'd finally grasped that my marriage was over. It had been coming for months, years really, but now I knew. I was headed to a small music festival which is hardly the place to be an emotional wreck, so I kept my inner world inconspicuous. I had girlfriends there, including Amy and Mary, so we determined to have fun despite everything that was ahead.

I was introduced to a tall, dark-haired friend of friends. Over that weekend we laughed and laughed. He made life delightful despite the circumstances.

Some weeks later, I was in his city. We wandered through the botanical gardens together and stopped for coconut water at an outdoor cafe. He was gazing away into the distance when it happened – talking about plants or Patagonia or particle physics. I felt something small dislodge in my heart, a feather lifting and drifting down into the core of my being. Suddenly I felt the most intense love for him. Whoever first thought to describe it that way – *falling in love* – must have felt that too. The *fall, the plummet, the tumble, the freedive*, the ludicrous unexpected descent into love. It was startling and unwanted.

Firstly, I was not attracted to him like that. It seems ridiculous now, but I wasn't. Only half an hour before, he'd told me he could not have a friendship with me. His marriage would not accommodate it. I was taken aback by that diversion in an otherwise impersonal conversation, but I agreed. I didn't need any complications, least of all his. I was already glimpsing the emotional healing required after twenty-two years of shared life. I knew *love*, impulsive romantic love, was no predictor of good outcomes. And I wasn't going to cause trouble in anyone else's life.

The feeling that thrummed in my heart had no place to go. It must remain quiet, private and secret. I didn't lean across and kiss his cheek, even if I wanted to. When the afternoon was done, we went our separate ways.

Love in the Time of Cholera by Gabriel Garcia Marquez is one of my favourite novels. Florentino Ariza waits all his life for Fermina Daza. Now I understood how it could happen. Falling in love like that, I couldn't have stopped it, and there was nothing to do about it. It was an aberration; a whimsical, warm autumnal moment that, as a writer, felt important to have experienced for future characters I might write about, but as for me – I must forget all about it.

We saw each other again two years later at the same festival with the same group of friends. Two years after that, we were all there again. There was love between us. Everyone could see it but we never discussed it. We listened to music and we laughed. When the festival was done, we said goodbye, both certain in our choices.

———

Five years after we first met, he arrived in Tasmania. He'd been having recurring dreams of our rainforests and he'd come to see those trees. Then he decided to stay. He moved to a place just moments from my home.

I'd been on my own since my marriage ended. I was healing. I'd had no interest in dating. I was finding my way back to a sense of wholeness. I had beloved friends and my dream life. I loved the sanctuary of my home, the hours of daily meditation. I had found my version of the monastery at last. I was living a secular life touched by the sacred. I was fulfilled.

Writing had finally become my full-time job, an unexpected breakthrough after *The Museum of Modern Love*. *Bruny* had been published, too. I was working on this memoir and a new novel.

But he was hard to resist. After I completed an arduous few months of writing, he took me away to a favourite ocean beach so I could revive myself in the surf. When I injured an ankle, he made funny messages, which he stuck on the bandage. He piggybacked me about for days, brought food, made tea. There was so much joy when we were together.

One evening he was sitting in a chair on my balcony. I suddenly saw him as I'd never seen him before. Maybe my resistance dropped away, or maybe it was something else. Maybe it was finally time. Because there he was. I *knew* those eyes. I *knew* that face. I thought, 'Oh, it's *you*!' A rush of intense attraction swept through me. It was disconcerting. How could it be *him*?

I didn't say anything, just as I hadn't mentioned the experience I'd had in the botanical gardens with him all those years ago. But not long after that, he told me he'd fallen in love with me at that first music festival. It was palpable and impossible. Through all these years, he'd tried to ignore it, but it wasn't going away. So here he was, if I'd have him.

One of my father's favourite expressions is *Every day is a good day*. Each day he gets to be with his family and friends, to walk a favourite path, listen to a favourite piece of music, read a loved book, be alive in this world, is a good day.

I said *yes*. I said yes to a wild wonderful love. It is late in life and we are beginning. Every day is a very good day.

HUMAN

The sacred is everywhere
We need only
Remember
To look
With sacred eyes.

TINA CHRISTENSEN

In the cold waters of the River Derwent, I swim through late winter and into spring in nothing but bathers. In the water, I am just another aquatic creature, akin to whale and dolphin, who must also rise to breathe. Today the sea is milky Prussian blue. Other days it's the green invitation of phthalo blue. I rarely miss a day.

It's a gift to my future self, all this swimming. I watch women in their sixties, seventies and eighties come down to the beach through the frosty months, on days when there is snow on the mountain, the sky is cloudless and the sun is warm away from the wind.

One woman, who may be in her nineties, puts out a plastic chair and drapes her towel over it. She swims in bathers and a cap, emerging some twenty minutes later as radiant as a sea goddess. Two other women breaststroke slowly half a kilometre and back, chatting and laughing. When I do it myself, brave the cold, brave it almost every day, I walk in up to my waist. I trail my hands in the water. My brain says, *You've got to be joking.* It lists every reason not to do this crazy thing. But then I go in.

At first, electricity shoots up my arms. My breath seesaws. There is no putting my head under. No freestyle. The air is too cold for wet hair and the water stings my face. I kick on my back. I breaststroke with care. I surrender my limbs and become swaying kelp. This is another sort of dance and I must learn the steps.

After ten minutes or so, something strange starts to happen. The shock departs. I can sense the chill against the outer layer of skin, but my organs are not cold. My body feels enlivened, as if this elixir of sea and sky is a balancing tonic, a healing force field of mysterious potential.

The cold has taught me a certain fearlessness. I procrastinate less. I need less. I am more grateful. I live more simply.

Sometimes the beach is closed because the sewerage plant upstream has had another spill. My parents ate fish from this enormous river, but no-one has done that for years now. Too many heavy metals.

As a child, I ate shellfish off the rocks and drank from rivers and lakes with no fear of contamination. When we fished, we never took more than we needed for a meal or two.

Our twenty-first-century bodies are soft, but we are hard on this planet. All we discard fills the land, all we pour away flows into the sea. Comfort is killing us. Disconnection, too.

I am an ocean swimmer, a coast dweller. My home is just seventy centimetres above the sea. The rhythms we've relied upon, the life we feel entitled to, it is all less certain.

HEART

The small woman
builds cages
for everyone she knows
While the sage,
who has to duck her head when the moon is low,
keeps dropping keys
all night long
for the beautiful
rowdy
prisoners

HAFIZ

I track down the coroner's report from the 1976 accident. Neither of my parents has ever seen it. I'm not sure why they were not sent a copy, or never requested one. Through a series of interviews with witnesses, the report recounts how three attempts were made to rescue Byron and Grandad on Lime Bay. First, the police boat broke down. Then a second boat went out, but the propellor was sheared off by an underwater rock. The first person clinging to the side of *Miss Wiggs* disappeared after twenty minutes. The second person disappeared after forty minutes. When a boat finally reached them, it was too late by ten minutes.

The onshore wind would have blown them to shore, but *Miss Wiggs*'s anchor had tumbled to the seabed and caught in the sandy bottom. They could have swum the distance if they'd started out right away, before the cold got to them, but Grandad always taught us to stay with the boat if we ever had an accident.

The coroner believed the boat was too small for the tiny two-stroke Seagull engine Grandad had recently purchased. The weight of the engine, the wet net of fish, and the wind starting to squall, it all contributed. They'd have both survived if they'd been wearing life jackets. They weren't mandatory back then, and Grandad believed they got in the way. Byron's was left on his bunk at the shack. He died wearing a jumper Mum had knitted for him.

—

Reading the coroner's report seems to ease something in both my father and my mother. Mum, especially, seems lighter. Perhaps knowing that every effort was made to save them, multiple attempts that all went wrong, was easier than thinking her own mother hadn't done enough to get help when the boat upturned. Or that Dad was to blame because Byron wanted to spend time with his grandfather.

People die in the sea often in Tasmania: young, old, fathers and daughters, grandfathers and sons. It's part of who we are. We are sea people, beholden to the strength of this vast blue ocean that surrounds us. Small in the face of it. Courageous, too.

—

On the anniversary of his birthday, I take Mum to Byron's grave. My sister and I organise this each year, taking turns. We take Dad, too, carefully timing it so there is no overlap.

On this anniversary, Mum says, 'I always come here alone.'

She is forgetful now, so I do not correct her. Instead, I say, 'We all come here alone, Mum.' Because we do, visiting when we need to, seeing our names on the headstone. Mum looks surprised, and then she nods, and weeps. It feels like the first time she acknowledges that we all lost him.

There is a little love in everything, it seems to me. Before Byron and Grandad died, my mother was the most wonderful mother in the world. I know not a day has gone by through all these years when she hasn't thought of Byron and missed him. She can never speak of him without tears.

—

At Christmas, my sister cooks lunch. To save us having two gatherings on that day, as we usually do, to accommodate the long winter of our parents' relationship, she invites them both. And suddenly here we all are. My sister's children, my children, my sister and me, Mum, Dad and my beloved. My sister has done the place settings and my son Byron sits between Mum and Dad. It is a poignant moment, seeing him there, knowing how he loves them both, knowing how they love him, this other Byron.

Mum is elegant as always, with jaunty Christmas jewellery for the occasion. Dad is refined and a little pale. When the conversation arrives at moments of reminiscence about child-hood things, Mum and Dad nod and agree with one another. They have spoken less than fifty words to each other in more than forty years. I've never heard my dad say a bad word about our mother, nor our mother say a good word about our father. But here they are at the Christmas table, both in their eighties, being gentle and gracious with one another.

—

There are memories to acknowledge if we are to learn to live with ourselves, events we revisit over and over, wondering who we are, and why we made those choices. There are always parts too painful to either forget or surrender, and parts that remain unknown until something or someone comes along who offers an invitation. Trauma is a form of haunting. In the darkness of life, there is an invitation for expansion.

We can imagine ourselves into a future we love. A future that inspires us. We can open ourselves to love in the face of fear, hurt, despair and betrayal. We can forgive in the face of pain, regret, outrage and resentment. Most of all, we can forgive ourselves. Forgiveness is a doorway to joy.

I've chosen to live with more and more joy. It hasn't stopped the pain – not the emotional pain nor the physical pain. But it has given me solid ground beneath it. I have learned to love the guidance and request of surrender, the invitation of boun-daries. The generosity of grace.

It's easy to be ashamed of the fuck-ups, mistakes and regrets, but in comparison to the magic, they really are quite small.

I'm not covering them up. I'm putting them in perspective. I'm forgiving myself for what it took to get here. I'm not frightened. I'm in love with it all. Even the bits that hurt. I am a human, being what we humans are. Fallible, fragile, strong, resilient, but reassured that all of this, all of it, is good.

It feels dangerous to be vulnerable, dangerous to forgive, dangerous to love, but this is where courage begins. It's risky to trust ourselves but we are emotional beings capable of intuition that can guide us in precise and wise ways. Our inner compass is rarely wrong. The privilege of being alive is fleeting, though the years seem long. To live knowing this is, perhaps, the greatest risk of all. My favourite socks say: *Carpe the fuck out of this diem.* I wear them on the hardest days, because the days we find courage are sometimes the greatest days of all.

I've come to accept that what I perceive as myself is actually something malleable, prone to change, to shed and re-construct, and to blossom at unlikely moments and for unlikely reasons. That seems to be the nature of being human. We become what we are story by story, piece by piece.

We are all capable of extraordinary things. To deny the invisible, the unseen but the deeply felt, is to deny our deepest intelligence. Despite my six-year-old self standing in the school-yard declaring myself available for service, I didn't expect to live a life so keen for answers. Maybe that's at the heart of all spirituality, be it accidental or deliberate, governed by a religion, or born of free thinking. Perhaps spirituality is another word for curiosity.

We don't need to hide the mysteries we experience, nor sweep them away unsung. We need to celebrate them. To relish our own unique story. To be human is a blessing and a burden. We've made the world unpredictable. We are of this Earth and it is of us. What will we do to earn our lives? It requires stamina to make new habits, to be bold in the face of seemingly implacable resistance, to trust our instincts, to protect what is vital for the future, to live without certainty.

We don't know how long we have, but here we are. This world is a beautiful, mysterious, magical place to live. It's time to awaken. To get brave and curious. If you're ready, here are a few suggestions . . .

Start with love.
Create ceremony.
Invite everyone.
Speak your truth.
Hold nothing back.
Swim in the beauty.
Dance, even a little.
Talk to each other.
Trust your instincts.
Practise silliness.
Love who you want to.
Forgive yourself.
Forgive one another.
Watch the sunrise.
Sing to the moon.

Read ten new books each year.
Be kind to all people, especially yourself.
Welcome simplicity.
Be grateful.
Choose joy.

SOURCES

Sky

'May I speak to you'
Hafiz, 'You Were Brave in that Holy War'.

Fire

'We do not "come into" this world'
Alan Watts, *The Book: On the Taboo Against Knowing Who You Are*,
Souvenir Press, London, 1969.

Moon

'The best is perhaps what we understand least'
C.S. Lewis, *A Grief Observed*, Seabury Presss, New York, © copyright 1961 C.S. Lewis Pte Ltd. Extract used with permission.

Salt Water

'There must be something strangely sacred in salt'
Khalil Gibran, *Sand and Foam*, Heinemann, London, 1927.

'Two Die in River'
The Mercury newspaper, 1 September 1976. Used with permission.

Prayer

'Stay close to anything'
Hafiz.

Heat

'What does it take to be a traveller?'
Anthony Weller, *Reader's Digest*, July 1984.

Opium

'Only those who will risk going too far'
T.S. Eliot, Preface to *Transit of Venus: Poems* by Harry Crosby, Black
    Sun Press, Paris, 1931.

Light

'I have always thirsted for knowledge'
Hermann Hesse, *Siddhartha*, B. Grasset, Paris, 1925.

Earth

'Initiation is a passage from one place to another'
Mark Wagner. Used with permission.

Piñon

'Whereas the sun dance is the time to pray for others'
White Heart. Used with permission.

Smoke

'It takes a deep commitment to change'
Ralph Ellison.

Skin

'The bark of the tree can feel like human skin'
White Heart. Used with permission.

Tree

'Two roads diverged in a wood'
Robert Frost, 'The Road Not Taken', Henry Holt & Company, New
York, 1916.

Rainbow

'The original sin is seriousness'
Osho, *Osho Teachings*. Used with permission.

Mountain

'Life is no "brief candle" for me'
George Bernard Shaw.

Forest

'Never be afraid to tread the path alone'
Eileen Caddy, *Footprints on the Path*, published by Findhorn Press,
© 1991. All rights reserved. www.innertraditions.com. Reprinted
with permission of the publisher.

Robin Wall Kimmerer, *Braiding Sweetgrass: Indigenous Wisdom,
Scientific Knowledge, and the Teachings of Plants*, Milkweed
Editions, Minneapolis, 2013.

Dolphins

'How inappropriate to call this planet Earth'
Arthur C. Clarke, *Dolphin Island*, Gollancz, London, 1963.
    Reproduced with permission of the Licensor through PLSclear.

Art

'Beware; for I am fearless'
Mary Shelley, *Frankenstein*, Lackington, Hughes, Harding, Mavor &
Jones, London, 1818.

Elephant

'Wear your heart on your skin in this life'

Sylvia Plath, *Johnny Panic and the Bible of Dreams: Short Stories, Prose, and Diary Excerpts*, 1977. Used with permission of the publishers, Faber and Faber Ltd.

'We should not be afraid of suffering'
Thich Nhat Hanh, *The Art of Living: Peace and Freedom in the Here and Now,* Random House, London, 2017.

Garden
'When life seems most impossible'
Tina Christensen, artist, tinachristensen.au.

Human
'The sacred is everywhere'
Tina Christensen, artist, tinachristensen.au.

The chapter 'Human' was written as a collaboration with artist Michaye Boulter for the Bett Gallery. It was published with the paintings of Michaye Boulter in a limited series of handmade books created by Penny Carey-Wells and Diane Perndt of Cloud Design. It was published in a similar form in *Island* magazine, edition 163.

Heart
'The small woman'
Hafiz, 'Dropping Keys'

WITH GRATITUDE

Heartfelt gratitude to everyone who has played a part in this story – those named and unnamed, and everyone in the invisible places between sentences and chapters. To this world of trees, animals, plants, oceans and mountains, rocks, rivers and skies that have been the nourishment of my life. To the friends who read early drafts. To the publishing team at Allen & Unwin headed by Jane Palfreyman – editors Ali Lavau and Christa Munns, publicist Christine Farmer, the designers, proofreaders, marketing team and management – who have given my work a home across seven books now. To Jenn Plapp for chasing permissions. To my agent of more than twenty years Gaby Naher. To the people of lutruwita – my Tasmanian community who have followed me down every pathway my work has explored. To my fellow writers who share this creative world with me – I admire you all. To all the readers near and far who have discovered my books, shared them with friends, and who have sent beautiful messages. To my three children who live at the heart of my life. To my mother and father, sister and brother and all my extended family. And to my beloved Evan who has shared the crafting of this work with such joy and tenderness. Love is good.